LATIN AMERICA

Fiction & Poetry
in Translation

———

Compiled by
SUZANNE JILL LEVINE

Center for Inter-American Relations
NEW YORK

The Center is a non-profit, tax-exempt
membership corporation financed by
foundation support, membership dues, and
corporate and individual gifts.

Contents

Preface

This list of books by authors from Spanish- and Portuguese-speaking countries of the Western Hemisphere is designed to help students, teachers and scholars of Latin American literature. We have attempted to bring together in one volume, information about works of contemporary fiction and poetry published in English in the United States through December 1969.

We hope that this compilation will be of use to all those interested in Latin America.

The Center for Inter-American Relations is reviewing the need for additional volumes for other areas of the hemisphere.

José Guillermo Castillo
Director, Literature Program
Center for Inter-American Relations

COMPILER'S NOTES:

* after title = book is out of print. Books are considered out of print according to Bowker's *1969 Books in Print*, except in a few cases where other information was available. The price of most of the out of print books has been omitted.

When the original title of a book does not appear, it is either because it is an anthology or a selection from different works.

Books by the same author are listed in order of publication.

I would like to thank Almir de Campos Bruneti, instructor of Portuguese at Yale University, for assistance in research on Brazilian literature, Marjorie Engber and Constance Campbell for valuable help with the indexes, and the Library of Congress Reference Department for its aid in making available scarce information.

Of special value in preparing this edition were the following works: *Brazil, Portugal, and other Portuguese-speaking lands; a list of books primarily in English*, by Francis M. Rogers and David T. Haberly (Harvard University Press, Cambridge, 1968); *Latin American Prose in English Translation* (Pan American Union, Washington, 1964); *Latin American Poetry in English Translation* (1965) by Claude L. Hulet and *Latin American Literature* (Widener Library Series, Cambridge, 1969).

S.J.L.

I. Anthologies

1 *AN ANTHOLOGY OF CONTEMPORARY LATIN AMERICAN POETRY**
Edited by Dudley Fitts (bilingual edition)
New Directions, Norfolk, 1942. 677 pp.

POETS:

Xavier Abril *Peru*
Martín Adán *Peru*
Carlos Drummond de Andrade
  Brazil
Eduardo Anguita *Chile*
Rafael Arévalo Martínez
  Guatemala
Rafael Alberto Arrieta *Argentina*
Miguel Angel Asturias *Guatemala*
Manuel Bandeira *Brazil*
Yolanda Bedregal de Cónitzer
  Bolivia
Jorge Luis Borges *Argentina*
Enrique Bustamente y Ballivián
  Peru
Luis Cané *Argentina*
Wilberto L. Cantón *Mexico*
Luis Cardoza y Aragón *Guatemala*
Eduardo Carranza *Colombia*
Jorge Carrera Andrade *Ecuador*
Alejandro Carrión *Ecuador*
Ronald de Carvalho *Brazil*
Oscar Castro Z. *Chile*
Menotti Del Picchia *Brazil*
Otto D'Sola *Venezuela*
José María Eguren *Peru*
Gonzalo Escudero *Ecuador*
Genaro Estrada *Mexico*
Rafael Estrada *Costa Rica*
José Miguel Ferrer *Venezuela*
Eugenio Florit *Cuba*
Jacinto Fombona Pachano
  Venezuela

Luis L. Franco *Argentina*
Oliverio Girondo *Argentina*
Gilberto González y Contreras
  El Salvador
Enrique Gonzalez Martínez
  Mexico
José Gorostiza *Mexico*
Nicolás Guillén *Cuba*
Alfonso Gutiérrez Hermosillo
José Ramón Heredia *Venezuela*
Demetrio Herrera S. *Panama*
Efraín Huerta *Mexico*
Vicente Huidobro *Chile*
Roberto Ibáñez *Uruguay*
Juana de Ibarbourou *Uruguay*
Claudia Lars *El Salvador*
José Lezama Lima *Cuba*
Jorge de Lima *Brazil*
Luis Carlos López *Colombia*
Francisco López Merino *Argentina*
Leopoldo Marechal *Argentina*
Rafael Maya *Colombia*
Murilo Mendes *Brazil*
Francisco Méndez *Nicaragua*
Rafael Méndez Dorich *Peru*
Gabriela Mistral *Chile*
Manuel Moreno Jimeno *Peru*
César Moro *Peru*
Conrado Nalé Roxlo *Argentina*
Pablo Neruda *Chile*
Salvador Novo *Mexico*
Silvina Ocampo *Argentina*
R. Olivares Figueroa *Venezuela*

Carlos Oquendo de Amat   *Peru*
Emilio Oribe   *Uruguay*
Bernardo Ortiz de Montellano
  Mexico
Raúl Otero Reiche   *Bolivia*
Miguel Otero Silva   *Venezuela*
Germán Pardo García   *Colombia*
Octavio Paz   *Mexico*
Regino Pedroso   *Cuba*
Carlos Pellicer   *Mexico*
Enrique Pena Barrenechea   *Peru*
Alejandro Peralta   *Peru*
Ildefonso Pereda Valdés   *Uruguay*
Angel Miguel Queremel   *Venezuela*
Alfonso Reyes   *Mexico*
Pablo de Rokha   *Chile*

Winétt de Rokha   *Chile*
Hipólito Sánchez Quell   *Paraguay*
Salomón de la Selva   *Nicaragua*
Alfonsina Storni   *Argentina*
Constantino Suasnavar   *Honduras*
César Tiempo   *Argentina*
Jaime Torres Bodet   *Mexico*
Rafael Heliodoro Valle   *Honduras*
César Vallejo   *Peru*
José Varallanos   *Peru*
Emilio Vásquez   *Peru*
Pedro Juan Vignale   *Argentina*
Xavier Villaurrutia   *Mexico*
Emilio Adolfo von Westphalen
  Peru
Luis Fabio Xammar   *Peru*

TRANSLATORS:
John Peale Bishop, Blanca López Castellón, Milton Ben Davis, Angel Flores,
Dudley Fitts, Robert Stuart Fitzgerald, H. R. Hays, Langston Hughes, Rolfe
Humphries, Thelma Lamb, Muna Lee de Muñoz Marín, Lloyd Mallan,
Richard O'Connell, Dudley Poore, José Rodríguez Feo, Joseph Staples,
Donald Devenish Walsh.

This anthology also includes works by other writers.

2   *ANTHOLOGY OF MEXICAN POETRY*
Edited by Octavio Paz. Translated by Samuel Beckett
Indiana University Press, Bloomington, 1965. 213 pp. $6.00, $1.95
(Indiana Poetry Paperback)

POETS:
Manuel Acuña
Juan Ruiz de Alarcón
Ignacio Manuel Altamirano
Bernardo de Balbuena
Matías de Bocanegra
Fernando de Córdova y Bocanegra
Salvador Díaz Mirón
Manuel M. Flores
Fernán González de Eslava
Francisco González León
Enrique González Martínez

Miguel de Guevara
Manuel Gutiérrez Nájera
Francisco A. de Icaza
Sor Juana Inés de la Cruz
Rafael López
Ramón López Velarde
José Manuel Martínez de Navarrete
Amado Nervo
Manuel José Othón
Joaquín Arcadio Pagaza
Manuel de la Parra

8

José Peón y Contreras
José Joaquín Pesado
Ignacio Ramírez
Efrén Rebolledo
Alfonso Reyes
Vicente Riva Palacio
Ignacio Rodríguez Galván

Luis de Sandoval y Zapata
Justo Sierra
Carlos de Sigüenza y Góngora
José Juan Tablada
Francisco de Terrazas
Luis G. Urbina

3 ANTHOLOGY OF MEXICAN POETS: FROM THE EARLIEST TIMES TO THE PRESENT DAY*

Translated by Edna Worthley Underwood
The Mosher Press, Portland, 1932. 332 pp.

POETS:

Manuel Acuña
Juan Ruiz de Alarcón
Wenceslao Alpuche
Ignacio M. Altamirano
Ricardo Arenales
Roberto Argüellos Bringas
Carlos Barrera
José M. Bustillos
Fernando Calderón
María Enriqueta Camarillo y Roa de
    Pereyra
Rubén M. Campos
Manuel Carpio
Joaquín D. Casasús
E. A. Chávez
Eduardo Colin
Felipe T. Contreras
José Peón Contreras
Francisco G. Cosmes
Juan Díaz Covarrubias
Agustín F. Cuenca
Balbino Dávalos
Juan B. Delgado
Rafael Delgado
Manuel Díaz Mirón
Salvador Díaz Mirón
Genaro Estrada

José Joaquín Fernández de Lizardi
Enrique Fernández Granados
Manuel M. Flores
José D. Frías
F. González Guerrero
Enrique González Martínez
Enrique González Rojo
José Gorostiza
Manuel Gutiérrez Nájera
Francisco A. de Icaza
Luciano Joublanc Rivas
Sor Juana Inés de la Cruz
Manuel Larrañaga Portugal
Rafael López
Ramón López Velarde
Rafael Lozano, Jr.
Ignacio M. Luchichi
Manuel V. Maples Arce
Ignacio Mariscal
Ignacio Martes de Oca
Miguel Gerónimo Martínez
Antonio Médiz Bolio
Francisco Monterde
Fray Manuel Navarrete
Amado Nervo
José J. Novelo
Salvador Novo

Francisco M. Olaguibel	José María Roa Bárcena
Manuel Olaguibel	Luis Rosado Vega
Bernardo Ortiz de Montellano	José Rosas Moreno
Manuel José Othón	Juan Manuel Ruiz Esparza
Gilberto Owen	Franz Sáenz Azcorra
Joaquín Arcadio Pagaza	Justo Sierra
Manuel de la Parra	José Juan Tablada
Carlos Pellicer	Joaquín Téllez
José Peón y Contreras	Francisco de Terrazas
Pedro I. Pérez Piña	Jaime Torres Bodet
Juan de Dios Peza	Pantaleón Tovar
Guillermo Prieto	Luis G. Urbina
Ignacio Ramirez	Rodolfo Usigli
Efrén Rebolledo	Jesús E. Valenzuela
Alfonso Reyes	Juan Valle
Vicente Riva Palacio	Xavier Villaurrutia
José Pablo Rivas	Rafael Enrique Zayos

4 AN ANTHOLOGY OF SPANISH POETRY FROM GARCILASO TO GARCÍA LORCA
Edited by Angel Flores (bilingual edition)
Anchor Books, Garden City, 1961. 516 pp. $1.45 (paper)

POETS:

Rubén Darío *Nicaragua*	Sor Juana Inés de la Cruz *Mexico*
Manuel González Prada *Peru*	Gabriela Mistral *Chile*

TRANSLATORS:
Kate Flores, Muriel Kittel, Samuel Beckett, Constance Urdang, William M. Davis, Anita Volland, John Crow, Denise Levertov, Doreen Bell, Charles Guenther, Muna Lee.

This anthology also includes works by other poets.

5 BRAZILIAN TALES*
Translated by Isaac Goldberg
The Four Seas Co., Boston, 1921. 149 pp.

WRITERS:

Carmen Dolores	José Medeiros e Albuquerque
Joaquim María Machado de Assis	Coelho Neto

6 *CHILE: AN ANTHOLOGY OF NEW WRITING*
Edited and translated by Miller Williams
Kent State University Press, Kent, 1968. 128 pp. $5.00, $1.95 (paper)

WRITERS:

Miguel Arteche
Efraín Barquero
Rolando Cárdenas
Boli Délano
Luisa Johnson
Enrique Lihn

Pablo Neruda
Alberto Rubio
Raúl Ruiz
Antonio Skarmeta
Jorge Teillier
Armando Uribe Arce

7 *CON CUBA: AN ANTHOLOGY OF CUBAN POETRY
OF THE LAST SIXTY YEARS*
Edited by Nathaniel Tarn (bilingual edition)
Cape Goliard Press, London; Grossman Publishers, New York, 1969.
144 pp. $4.50, $2.50 (paper)

POETS:

Rafael Alcides
Orlando Alomá
Miguel Barnet
Victor Casaus
Belkis Cuza Malé
Manuel Díaz Martínez
Eliseo Diego
Froilán Escobar
Samuel Feijóo
Lina de Feria
David Fernández
Pablo Armando Fernández
Roberto Fernández Retamar
Gerardo Fulleda León
Fina García Marruz

Félix Guerra
Fayad Jamís
José Lezama Lima
Eduardo Lolo
César López
Luis Marré
Nancy Morejón
Luis Rogelio Nogueras
Pedro de Oraá
Heberto Padilla
Félix Pita Rodríguez
Isel Rivero
Guillermo Rodríguez Rivera
Luis Suardíaz
Cintio Vitier

TRANSLATORS:

Lionel Kearns, Nathaniel Tarn, Anthony Kerrigan, Tom Raworth, Tim
Reynolds, Donald Gardner, David Ossman, Carl Hagen, Adrian Mitchell,
Elinor Randall, Margaret Randall, Stephen Schwartz.

8 FIESTA IN NOVEMBER; STORIES FROM LATIN AMERICA*
Edited by Angel Flores and Dudley Poore
Houghton Mifflin, Boston, 1942. 608 pp.
(a selection of novels and short stories)

WRITERS:

Demetrio Aguilera Malta *Ecuador*
Jorge Amado *Brazil*
Armando Arriaza *Chile*
Eduardo Barrios *Chile*
Adolfo Costa du Rels *Bolivia*
Juan Carlos Dávalos *Argentina*
José Díez-Canseco *Peru*
Héctor I. Eandi *Argentina*
Eduardo Mallea *Argentina*

Rafael Maluenda Labarca *Chile*
Guillermo Meneses *Venezuela*
Horacio Quiroga *Uruguay*
Salvador Reyes *Chile*
José Rubén Romero *Mexico*
Rogelio Sinán *Panama*
Luis Tablanca *Colombia*
Arturo Uslar Pietri *Venezuela*
Abraham Valdelomar *Peru*

TRANSLATORS:

Alis De Sola, Enid Eder Perkins, Harriet de Onís, Alida Malkus, Angel Flores, Joan Coyne, Donald Walsh, Drake de Kay, Dorothy Conzelman, Elizabeth Wallace, R. Selden Rose, Francisco Aguilera.

9 FROM THE GREEN ANTILLES*
Edited by Barbara Howes
Macmillan, New York, 1966. 368 pp. $6.95

WRITERS:

Juan Bosch *Dominican Republic*
Lydia Cabrera *Cuba*
Alejo Carpentier *Cuba*
Eliseo Diego *Cuba*

Nicolás Guillén *Cuba*
Carlos Montenegro *Cuba*
Lino Novás Calvo *Cuba*

TRANSLATORS:

Lionel Abel, Hubert Van Den Bergh, Patrick Bowles, Alex Brotherston, Estelle Reed Debrot, Roy Edwards, Frances Frenaye, Langston Hughes, Merloyd Lawrence, Joan Maclean, Frances Willard von Maltitz, Zoila Nelken, Harriet de Onís, R. R. Symonds, Eva Thoby-Marcelin, Nick Vandemoer, Louis Varese.

This anthology also includes works by other Caribbean writers.

10 *HISPANIC ANTHOLOGY: POEMS TRANSLATED FROM THE SPANISH BY ENGLISH AND NORTH AMERICAN POETS** Edited by Thomas Walsh (bilingual edition) Putnam, New York, 1920. 779 pp.

POETS:

Olegario Victor Andrade *Argentina*
R. Arévalo Martínez *Guatemala*
Andrés Bello *Venezuela*
Rufino Blanco Fombona *Venezuela*
Mariano Brull *Cuba*
José Eusebio Caro *Colombia*
Ricardo Carrasquilla *Colombia*
Julián del Casal *Cuba*
José Santos Chocano *Peru*
Luis Felipe Contardo *Chile*
Rubén Darío *Nicaragua*
Balbino Dávalos *Mexico*
Salvador Díaz Mirón *Mexico*
Alonso de Ercilla y Zúñiga *Chile*
Fabio Fiallo *Dominican Republic*
Julio Flores *Colombia*
Gertrudis Gómez de Avellaneda *Cuba*
Antonio Gómez Restrepo *Colombia*
Enrique González Martínez *Mexico*
Alfonso Guillén Zelaya *Honduras*
Manuel Gutiérrez Nájera *Mexico*
José María Heredia *Cuba*
Enrique Hernández Míyares *Cuba*
Julio Herrera y Reissig *Uruguay*
Dmitri Ivanovitch *Colombia*
Sor Juana Inés de la Cruz *Mexico*
Samuel A. Lillo *Chile*
Luis C. López *Colombia*

René López *Cuba*
Leopoldo Lugones *Argentina*
Manuel Magallanes Moure *Chile*
Rafael María de Mendive *Cuba*
Gabriela Mistral *Chile*
Ernesto Montenegro *Chile*
Amado Nervo *Mexico*
Luis G. Ortiz *Mexico*
Joaquín Arcadio Pagaza *Mexico*
Ricardo Palma *Peru*
Felipe Pardo *Peru*
Bulhâo Pato *Brazil*
Carlos Pezoa Véliz *Chile*
Martine Pierre de Poo *Cuba*
Ramón Pimentel Coronel *Venezuela*
Rafael Pombo *Colombia*
José Manuel Poveda *Cuba*
Pedro Requena Legarreta *Mexico*
José Rosas Moreno *Mexico*
Antonio Sellén *Cuba*
José Asunción Silva *Colombia*
Victor Domingo Silva *Chile*
José Juan Tablada *Mexico*
Diego Vicente Tejera *Cuba*
Luis G. Urbina *Mexico*
Guillermo Valencia *Colombia*
José E. Valenzuela *Mexico*
Faqundes Varella *Brazil*
Daniel de la Vega *Chile*
Juan José Velgas *Chile*

TRANSLATORS:

John Bowring, Peter H. Goldsmith, Roderick Gill, Thomas Walsh, William Cullen Bryant, H. W. Longfellow, Alice Stone Blackwell, Elijah Clarence

Hills, Garret Strange, Alfred Coester, Jorge Godoy, Muna Lee, John Pierrepont Rice, Ernest F. Lucas, L. E. Elliott, William G. Williams, Joseph I. C. Clarke.

This anthology also includes works by other poets.

11 *LATIN AMERICAN WRITING TODAY*
Edited by J. M. Cohen
Penguin Books, Baltimore, 1967. 267 pp. $3.25

WRITERS:

Breno Accioly *Brazil*
Carlos Drummond de Andrade *Brazil*
Mario Benedetti *Uruguay*
Jorge Luis Borges *Argentina*
Guillermo Cabrera Infante *Cuba*
Onelio Jorge Cardoso *Cuba*
Alejo Carpentier *Cuba*
Rosario Castellanos *Mexico*
Alí Chumacero *Mexico*
Julio Cortázar *Argentina*
José Donoso *Chile*
Pablo Armando Fernández *Cuba*
Carlos Fuentes *Mexico*
Gabriel García Márquez *Colombia*
Alberto Girri *Argentina*
Enrique Lihn *Chile*

C. Vasconcelos Maia *Brazil*
João Cabral de Melo Neto *Brazil*
Gabriela Mistral *Chile*
Ricardo E. Molinari *Argentina*
Marco Antonio Montes de Oca *Mexico*
Vinicius de Moraes *Brazil*
Pablo Neruda *Chile*
Juan Carlos Onetti *Uruguay*
José Emilio Pacheco *Mexico*
Nicanor Parra *Chile*
Octavio Paz *Mexico*
Carlos Pellicer *Mexico*
João Guimarães Rosa *Brazil*
Juan Rulfo *Mexico*
Jaime Sabines *Mexico*
César Vallejo *Peru*

TRANSLATORS:

Elizabeth Bishop, Paul Blackburn, Arthur Boyars, J. G. Brotherston, Ashley Brown, J. M. Cohen, Doris Dana, Jean Franco, John Gibson, Henry Gifford, R. P. Joscelyne, Lysander Kemp, W. S. Merwin, Christopher Middleton, Charles Tomlinson.

12 *MEXICAN POETRY: AN ANTHOLOGY**
Edited by Isaac Goldberg
Haldeman-Julius, Girard, 1925. 64 pp. (Little Blue Book no. 810)

POETS:

Manuel Acuña
Rafael Cabrera

María Enriqueta Camarillo y Roa
Agustín F. Cuenca

Balbino Dávalos
Salvador Díaz Mirón
Enrique Fernández Granados
Manuel M. Flores
Enrique González Martínez
Manuel Gutiérrez Nájera
Sor Juana Inés de la Cruz

Amado Nervo
Manuel José Othón
José M. Pino
José Rosas Moreno
José Juan Tablada
Luis G. Urbina
Jesús E. Valenzuela

TRANSLATORS:
Peter H. Goldsmith, William Cullen Bryant, Alice Stone Blackwell, Isaac
Goldberg, Thomas Walsh.

13 *MODERN BRAZILIAN POETRY: AN ANTHOLOGY*
Edited and translated by John Nist and Yolanda Leite
University of Indiana Press, Bloomington, 1962, 1968 (Kraus Reprint). 175 pp. $9.50

POETS:
Carlos Drummond de Andrade
Mario de Andrade
Manuel Bandeira
Paulo Bomfim
Jorge de Lima
Cecilia Meireles

Joâo Cabral de Melo Neto
Murilo Mendes
Vinicius de Moraes
Cassiano Ricardo
Augusto Frederico Schmidt
Domingo Carvalho da Silva

14 *MODERN BRAZILIAN SHORT STORIES*
Edited and translated by William L. Grossman
University of California Press, Berkeley, 1967. 167 pp. $4.95

WRITERS:
Mario de Andrade
Darcy Azambuja
José Carlos Cavalcanti Borges
Ribeiro Couto
Aurélio Buarque de Holanda
Luís Jardim
Clarice Lispector
Aníbal Machado
Antônio de Alcântara Machado

R. Magalhães Júnior
Vasconcelos Maia
Marília São Paulo Penna e Costa
Rachel de Queiroz
Dinah Silveira de Queiroz
Graciliano Ramos
Marques Rebêlo
Joâo Guimarães Rosa

15 *MODERN POETRY FROM SPAIN AND*
LATIN AMERICA
Translated by Nan Braymer and Lillian Lowenfels
Corinth Books, New York, 1964. 63 pp. $1.45 (paper)

POETS:

Nicolás Guillén   *Cuba*   Salomón de la Selva   *Nicaragua*
Agustín Millares   *Mexico*   César Vallejo   *Peru*

This anthology also includes works by other poets.

16 *THE MODERNIST TREND IN SPANISH AMERICAN*
*POETRY**
Compiled and translated by George Dundas Craig
University of California Press, Berkeley, 1934. 347 pp.

POETS:

Enrique Banchs   *Argentina*   Gabriela Mistral   *Chile*
Jorge Luis Borges   *Argentina*   Pablo Neruda   *Chile*
José Santos Chocano   *Peru*   Amado Nervo   *Mexico*
Rubén Darío   *Nicaragua*   Carlos Pezoa Véliz   *Chile*
Enrique González Martínez   Pedro Prado   *Chile*
  Mexico   José Asunción Silva   *Colombia*
Juan Guzmán Cruchaga   *Chile*   Víctor Domingo Silva   *Chile*
Julio Herrera y Reissig   *Uruguay*   Alfonsina Storni   *Argentina*
Vicente Huidobro   *Chile*   Arturo Torres-Ríoseco   *Chile*
Ricardo Jaimes Freyre   *Bolivia*   Guillermo Valencia   *Colombia*
Leopoldo Lugones   *Argentina*

17 *NEW VOICES OF HISPANIC AMERICA;*
*AN ANTHOLOGY**
Edited and translated by Darwin J. Flakoll and Claribel Alegría
Beacon Press, Boston, 1962. 226 pp.
(A selection of fiction and poetry, including original text of poems)

WRITERS:

Eduardo Anguita   *Chile*   Rosario Castellanos   *Mexico*
Juan José Arreola   *Mexico*   Carlos Castro Saavedra   *Colombia*
Mario Benedetti   *Uruguay*   Julio Cortazár   *Argentina*
Rubén Bonifaz Nuño   *Mexico*   José Donoso   *Chile*
Ernesto Cardenal   *Nicaragua*   Elba Fábregas   *Argentina*
Alfredo Cardona Peña   *Costa Rica*   Otto Raul González   *Guatemala*

Ida Gramcko   *Venezuela*
Dora Guerra   *El Salvador*
Fayad Jamís   *Cuba*
Enrique Lihn   *Chile*
Hugo Lindo   *El Salvador*
Ernesto Mejía Sánchez   *Nicaragua*
Porfirio Meneses   *Peru*
Augusto Monterroso   *Guatemala*
H. A. Murena   *Argentina*
Alberto Ordoñez Argüello
   Nicaragua
Adalberto Ortiz   *Ecuador*
Nicanor Parra   *Chile*
Joaquín Pasos   *Nicaragua*

Octavio Paz   *Mexico*
Augusto Roa Bastos   *Paraguay*
Gonzalo Rojas   *Chile*
José Guillermo Ros Zanet   *Panama*
Alberto Rubio   *Chile*
Juan Rulfo   *Mexico*
Sebastián Salazar Bondy   *Peru*
Hugo Salazar Tamariz   *Ecuador*
Nivaria Tejera   *Cuba*
Blanca Varela   *Peru*
Idea Vilariño   *Uruguay*
Ida Vitale   *Uruguay*
Cintio Vitier   *Cuba*
María Elena Walsh   *Argentina*

This anthology also includes works by other poets.

18   *NINE LATIN AMERICAN POETS*
Edited and translated by Rachel Benson (bilingual edition)
Las Americas, New York, 1968. 359 pp. $6.50

POETS:

José Gorostiza   *Mexico*
Vicente Huidobro   *Chile*
Pablo Neruda   *Chile*
Octavio Paz   *Mexico*

Carlos Pellicer   *Mexico*
Alfonsina Storni   *Argentina*
César Vallejo   *Peru*
Xavier Villaurrutia   *Mexico*

19   *PAN AMERICAN POEMS, AN ANTHOLOGY**
Compiled by Agnes Blake Poor
The Gorham Press, Boston, 1918. 80 pp.

POETS:

Francisco Acuña de Figueroa
   Uruguay
Juan Cruz Varela   *Argentina*
Augustín F. Cuenca   *Mexico*
Rubén Darío   *Nicaragua*
Antonio Gonçalves Dias   *Brazil*
Esteban Echeverría   *Argentina*
Santiago Escuti Orrego   *Chile*
Arturo Giménez Pastor   *Argentina*
Gertrudis Gómez de Avellaneda
   Cuba

José María Heredia   *Cuba*
Hermógenes Irisarri   *Chile*
D. A. Lozano   *Venezuela*
Manuel María Madiedo   *Colombia*
Diego Maisias y Calle   *Peru*
Francisco Manuel   *Brazil*
José Mármol   *Argentina*
Pedro J. Naón   *Argentina*
José Joaquín de Olmedo   *Ecuador*
Mariano Ramallo   *Bolivia*
José Rivera Indarte   *Argentina*

Bruno Seabra   *Brazil*
Narcíso Tondreau   *Chile*
Florencio Varela   *Argentina*
Domingo de Vivero   *Peru*

Ethelberto Zegarra Ballón   *Peru*
Juan Zorrilla de San Martín
   Uruguay

TRANSLATORS:
Agnes Blake Poor, William Cullen Bryant.

This anthology also includes works by other poets.

20   *THE PENGUIN BOOK OF SPANISH VERSE**
Edited and translated by John Michael Cohen (bilingual edition with
   plain prose translations)
Penguin Books, Baltimore, 1956. 441 pp.

POETS:
Jorge Carrera Andrade   *Ecuador*
Alí Chumacero   *Mexico*
Rubén Darío   *Nicaragua*
Salvador Díaz Mirón   *Mexico*
Enrique González Martínez
   Mexico
Nicolás Guillén   *Cuba*
Julio Herrera y Reissig   *Uruguay*
Sor Juana Inés de la Cruz   *Mexico*
Ramón López Velarde   *Mexico*

Ricardo E. Molinari   *Argentina*
Pablo Neruda   *Chile*
Salvador Novo   *Mexico*
Silvina Ocampo   *Argentina*
Manuel José Othón   *Mexico*
Octavio Paz   *Mexico*
Alberto Quintero Álvarez   *Mexico*
Alfonso Reyes   *Mexico*
César Vallejo   *Peru*
Xavier Villaurrutia   *Mexico*

This anthology also includes works by other poets.

21   *PRIZE STORIES FROM LATIN AMERICA**
Preface by Arturo Uslar Pietri
Doubleday paperback (Dolphin), New York, 1964. 383 pp. $1.45

WRITERS:
Laura del Castillo   *Argentina*
Haroldo Pedro Conti   *Argentina*
Marco Denevi   *Argentina*
Alfonso Echeverría   *Chile*
Ramón Ferreira López   *Cuba*
Faustino González-Aller   *Cuba*

Carlos Martínez Moreno   *Uruguay*
Tomás Mojarro   *Mexico*
Juan Carlos Onetti   *Uruguay*
Carlos Rozas Larraín   *Chile*
Rolando Venturini   *Argentina*

TRANSLATORS:
Paul Blackburn, Alfonso Echeverría, Lysander Kemp, Izaak A. Langnas,
Harriet de Onís, Jerome Rothenberg, David Ruben.

22 SHORT STORIES OF LATIN AMERICA*
Edited by Arturo Torres-Ríoseco
Translated by Zoila Nelken and Rosalie Torres-Ríoseco
Las Americas, New York, 1963. 203 pp.

WRITERS:

Ciro Alegría *Peru*
María Luisa Bombal *Chile*
Jorge Luis Borges *Argentina*
Alejo Carpentier *Cuba*
Guadalupe Dueñas *Mexico*
Andrés Henestrosa *Mexico*
Juan Marín *Chile*

Lino Novás Calvo *Cuba*
Alfredo Pareja Díez Canseco
 Ecuador
Félix Pita Rodríguez *Cuba*
Horacio Quiroga *Uruguay*
Manuel Rojas *Chile*
Agustín Yáñez *Mexico*

This anthology also includes works by other writers.

23 SOME SPANISH AMERICAN POETS
Edited by Isaac Goldberg
Translated by Alice Stone Blackwell (bilingual edition)
Greenwood Press, New York, 1968. 559 pp. $19.50

POETS:

Manuel Acuña *Mexico*
Almafuerte *Argentina*
Enrique Alvarez Henao *Colombia*
Olegario Victor Andrade
 Argentina
Rafael Arévalo Martínez
 Guatemala
Santiago Argüello *Nicaragua*
Andrés Bello *Venezuela*
Rufino Blanco Fombona
 Venezuela
Dulce María Borrero de Luján
 Cuba
Mario Bravo *Argentina*
Roberto Brenes Mesén *Costa Rica*
Bonifacio Byrne *Cuba*
Rafael Cabrera *Mexico*
José A. Calcaño *Venezuela*
José Eusebio Caro *Colombia*
Joaquín Castellanos *Argentina*
José Santos Chocano *Peru*

Luis F. Contardo *Chile*
Francisco Contreras *Chile*
Augustín F. Cuenca *Mexico*
Rubén Darío *Nicaragua*
Balbino Dávalos *Mexico*
Juan B. Delgado *Mexico*
Salvador Díaz Mirón *Mexico*
Luis L. Domínguez *Argentina*
Manuel Duque *Bolivia*
María Enriqueta *Mexico*
Demetrio Fábrega *Panama*
Enrique Fernández Granados
 Mexico
Fabio Fiallo *Dominican Republic*
Julio Flores *Colombia*
Manuel María Flores *Mexico*
Alberto Ghiraldo *Argentina*
Gertrudis Gómez de Avellaneda
 Cuba
Alfredo Gómez Jaime *Colombia*
Joaquín Gómez Vergara *Mexico*

Jorge González B.   *Chile*
Enrique González Martínez
   Mexico
Alejandro Guanes   *Paraguay*
Ricardo Gutiérrez   *Argentina*
Manuel Gutiérrez Nájera   *Mexico*
José María Heredia y Campuzano
   Cuba
Enrique Hernández Míyares   *Cuba*
Julio Herrera y Reissig   *Uruguay*
David Hine   *Costa Rica*
Jorge Hübner   *Chile*
Juana de Ibarbourou   *Uruguay*
Francisco A. de Icaza   *Mexico*
Ricardo Jaimes Freyre   *Bolivia*
Sor Juana Inés de la Cruz   *Mexico*
Leopoldo Lugones   *Argentina*
Luisa Luisi   *Uruguay*
M. Magallanes Moure   *Chile*
Mercedes Marín del Solar   *Chile*
Román Mayorga Rivas   *Salvador*
Gabriela Mistral   *Chile*
Bartolomé Mitre   *Argentina*
Amado Nervo   *Mexico*
Rafael Obligado   *Argentina*
José Joaquín de Olmedo   *Ecuador*
Luis G. Ortiz   *Mexico*

Manuel José Othón   *Mexico*
Benigno Palma   *Panama*
Ricardo Palma   *Peru*
Ramón de Palma y Romay   *Cuba*
Ignacio A. Pane   *Paraguay*
S. José M. Pino   *Mexico*
Rafael Pombo   *Colombia*
Pedro Prado   *Chile*
Carlos Augusto Salaverry   *Peru*
Justo Sierra   *Mexico*
José Asunción Silva   *Colombia*
Víctor Domingo Silva   *Chile*
Francisco Sosa   *Mexico*
Alfonsina Storni   *Argentina*
Jaime Torres Bodet   *Mexico*
Froylán Turcios   *Honduras*
Luis G. Urbina   *Mexico*
Salomé Ureña de Henríquez
   Santo Domingo
Diego Uribe   *Colombia*
Guillermo Valencia   *Colombia*
Jesús E. Valenzuela   *Mexico*
José León del Valle   *Mexico*
Daniel de la Vega   *Chile*
Juan Zorrilla de San Martín
   Uruguay

This anthology also includes works by other poets.

24 *SPANISH AMERICAN LITERATURE
   IN TRANSLATION. Vol. I*
Edited by Willis K. Jones
Frederick Ungar, New York, 1963. 356 pp. $7.50
(A selection of prose, poetry, and drama before 1888)

WRITERS:

José de Acosta   *Peru*
Manuel Acuña   *Mexico*
Ignacio Manuel Altamirano
   Mexico
"Amarilis"   *Peru*

Olegario Víctor Andrade
   Argentina
Bernardo de Balbuena   *Mexico*
Andrés Bello   *Venezuela*
Carlos Bello   *Chile*

Fray Bernardino de Sahagún *Mexico*
Alberto Blest Gana   *Chile*
Simón Bolívar   *Venezuela*
Estanislao del Campo   *Argentina*
José Eusebio Caro   *Colombia*
Pedro Cieza de León   *Peru*
Concolorcorvo   *Peru*
Juan Cruz Varela   *Argentina*
Bernal Díaz del Castillo   *Mexico*
Ruiz Díaz de Guzmán   *Paraguay*
Esteban Echeverría   *Argentina*
Alonso de Ercilla y Zúñiga   *Chile*
José Joaquín Fernández de Lizardi
Mexico
Manuel de Jesús Galván
Santo Domingo
Garcilaso de la Vega, Inca   *Peru*
Gertrudis Gómez de Avellaneda
Cuba
Camilo Henríquez   *Chile*
José María Heredia   *Cuba*
José Hernández   *Argentina*
Jorge Isaacs   *Colombia*
Sor Juana Inés de la Cruz   *Mexico*
Diego de Landa   *Mexico*
Joaquín Lorenzo Luaces   *Cuba*
José Mármol   *Argentina*
Clorinda Matto de Turner   *Peru*
Juan León Mera   *Ecuador*
José Jacinto Milanés y Fuentes
Cuba

Bartolomé Mitre   *Argentina*
Jerónimo de Monforte y Vera
Peru
Juan Montalvo   *Ecuador*
"Motolinía" (Fray Toribio de
Benavente)   *Mexico*
Francisco Morazán   *Honduras*
Alvar Nuñez Cabeza de Vaca
Mexico
Francisco Nuñez de Pineda y
Bascuñán   *Chile*
Rafael Obligado   *Argentina*
José Joaquín de Olmedo   *Ecuador*
Pedro de Oña   *Chile*
Alonso de Ovalle   *Chile*
Ricardo Palma   *Peru*
Manuel Payno   *Mexico*
José Peón y Contreras   *Mexico*
Vicente Pérez Rosales   *Chile*
"Plácido"   *Cuba*
Rafael Pombo   *Colombia*
Mariano Ramallo   *Bolivia*
Salvador Sanfuentes   *Chile*
Domingo Faustino Sarmiento
Argentina
Carlos de Sigüenza y Góngora
Mexico
Francisco de Terrazas   *Mexico*
Ramón Vial y Ureta   *Chile*
Cirilo Villaverde   *Cuba*
Juan Zorrilla de San Martin
Uruguay

TRANSLATORS:
(*Prose*) Delia Goetz, Sylvanus G. Morley, George Folsom, Willis K. Jones,
Buckingham Smith, Samuel Purchas, George Karnezis.
(*Poetry*) Susan Louise Shelby, Walter Owen, Read Bain, Charles M. Lan-
caster, Paul T. Manchester, James C. Bardin, Alfred Coester, Beatrice Gilman
Proske, Thomas Walsh, Agnes Blake Poor, Elijah C. Hills, William Cullen
Bryant, H. W. Hurlbut, Chesley M. Hutchings.
(*Drama*) Willis K. Jones, Elijah C. Hills.

This anthology also includes works by other writers.

24a *SPANISH AMERICAN LITERATURE
IN TRANSLATION. Vol. II*
Edited by Willis K. Jones
Frederick Ungar, New York, 1963. 469 pp. $8.50
(A selection of prose, poetry, and drama since 1888)

WRITERS:

Eduardo Acevedo Díaz   *Uruguay*
Antonio Acevedo Hernández   *Chile*
Demetrio Aguilera Malta   *Ecuador*
Isidora Aguirre   *Chile*
Ciro Alegría   *Peru*
Rafael Arévalo Martínez
   Guatemala
Alcides Arguedas   *Bolivia*
Lino Argüello   *Nicaragua*
Santiago Argüello Barreto
   Nicaragua
Mariano Azuela   *Mexico*
Enrique Banchs   *Argentina*
Eduardo Barrios   *Chile*
Rufino Blanco Fombona   *Venezuela*
Alberto Blest Gana   *Chile*
Jorge Luis Borges   *Argentina*
Marta Brunet   *Chile*
José Antonio Campos   *Ecuador*
Herib Campos Cervera   *Paraguay*
Jorge Carrera Andrade   *Ecuador*
Julián del Casal   *Cuba*
José Santos Chocano   *Peru*
Stella Corvalán   *Chile*
Carlos S. Damel   *Argentina*
Camilo Darthés   *Argentina*
Rubén Darío   *Nicaragua*
Salvador Díaz Mirón   *Mexico*
Samuel Eichelbaum   *Argentina*
Jorge Escobar Uribe   *Argentina*
Jacinto Fombona Pachano
   Venezuela
Eloy Fariña Núñez   *Paraguay*
Fabio Fiallo   *Dominican Republic*
Gastón Figueira   *Uruguay*
Rómulo Gallegos   *Venezuela*

José Joaquín Gamboa   *Mexico*
Enrique González Martínez   *Mexico*
Manuel González Prada   *Peru*
Alejandro Guanes   *Paraguay*
Nicolás Guillén   *Cuba*
Ricardo Güiraldes   *Argentina*
Eduardo Gutiérrez   *Argentina*
Manuel Gutiérrez Nájera   *Mexico*
Martín Luis Guzmán   *Mexico*
Juan Guzmán Cruchaga   *Mexico*
Enrique Hernández Míyares   *Cuba*
Julio Herrera y Reissig   *Uruguay*
Vicente Huidobro   *Chile*
Juana de Ibarbourou   *Uruguay*
Jorge Icaza   *Ecuador*
Ricardo Jaimes Freyre   *Bolivia*
Enrique Larreta   *Argentina*
Claudia Lars   *El Salvador*
Carmen Lira   *Costa Rica*
Luis Carlos López   *Colombia*
Gregorio López y Fuentes   *Mexico*
Ramón López Velarde   *Mexico*
Leopoldo Lugones   *Argentina*
Eduardo Mallea   *Argentina*
Rafael Maluenda Labarca   *Chile*
José Martí   *Cuba*
Enrique Méndez Calzada   *Argentina*
Gabriela Mistral   *Chile*
Guillermo Molinas Rolón
   Paraguay
Armando Moock   *Chile*
Francisco Navarro   *Mexico*
Pablo Neruda   *Chile*
Amado Nervo   *Mexico*
Juan E. O'Leary   *Paraguay*
Miguel Angel Osorio   *Colombia*

Octavio Paz *Mexico*
Regino Pedroso *Cuba*
Pedro E. Pico *Argentina*
Angel Pino *Chile*
Josefina Pla *Paraguay*
José J. Podestá *Argentina*
Pedro Prado *Chile*
Horacio Quiroga *Uruguay*
José Antonio Ramos *Cuba*
Alfonso Reyes *Mexico*
José María Rivarola Matto
  Paraguay
José Eustasio Rivera *Colombia*
Augusto Roa Bastos *Paraguay*
José Enrique Rodó *Uruguay*

Elvio Romero *Paraguay*
Florencio Sánchez *Uruguay*
Jose Asunción Silva *Colombia*
Medaro Angel Silva *Ecuador*
Fernán Silva Valdés *Uruguay*
Alfonsina Storni *Argentina*
César Tiempo *Argentina*
Jaime Torres Bodet *Mexico*
Froylán Turcios *Honduras*
César Uribe *Colombia*
Rodolfo Usigli *Mexico*
Guillermo Valencia *Colombia*
César Abraham Vallejo *Peru*
Julio Vicuña Cifuentes *Chile*
Hugo Wast *Argentina*

TRANSLATORS:

(*Poetry*) John Pierrepont Rice, Thomas Walsh, Alice Jane McVan, Muna Lee, Alice Stone Blackwell, Willis K. Jones, Read Bain, Chesley M. Hutchings, Beatrice Gilman Proske, Helen Eldridge Fish, Edna Worthley Underwood, H. R. Hays, Donald Malcolm, R. L. Maloney, Donald D. Walsh, Langston Hughes, Joseph Leonard Grucci, Ben F. Carruthers, Mary Newman, Paul T. Manchester, William G. Williams, Mary and C. V. Wicker, Lloyd Mallan, Jessie Read Wendell, Roderick Gill, Dorothy Conzelman, Isabel K. Macdermotte, Arturo Torres-Ríoseco, Garrett Strange, Elizabeth du Gue Trapier.

(*Prose*) Elizabeth Turner, Willis K. Jones, Elaine Schaefer, E. K. James, Robert Malloy, Linda Wilson, E. Munguía, Jr., Robert Alan Goldberg, Sheila Toye, B. Jane Johnson, Susan Louise Shelby, Marilyn Bauman, Hugo Manning, W. P. Negron, Astrid S. Hasbrouck, Robert Scott, Donald A. Yates, Edmund C. García.

(*Drama*) Carlos Escudero, Willis K. Jones, Maria Luisa Hurtado Delgado, David A. Flory, Carol Davis, Kathy Booker.

This anthology also includes works by other writers.

25 *SPANISH AMERICAN POETRY:*
    A BILINGUAL SELECTION
Compiled by Seymour Resnick
Harvey House, Irvington-on-Hudson, 1964. 96 pp. $3.50

POETS:

Manuel Acuña *Mexico*
José Eusebio Caro *Colombia*

José Santos Chocano *Peru*
Rubén Darío *Nicaragua*

Luis L. Domínguez *Argentina*
Alonso de Ercilla *Chile*
Fabio Fiallo *Dominican Republic*
Gertrudis Gómez de Avellaneda
  Cuba
Enrique González Martínez
  Mexico
Manuel González Prada *Peru*
Carlos Guido y Spano *Argentina*
Manuel Gutiérrez Nájera *Mexico*
José María Heredia *Cuba*
Juana de Ibarbourou *Uruguay*
Francisco Icaza *Mexico*

Sor Juana Inés de la Cruz *Mexico*
Leopoldo Lugones *Argentina*
José Martí *Cuba*
Mariano Melgar *Peru*
Gabriela Mistral *Chile*
Pablo Neruda *Chile*
Amado Nervo *Mexico*
José Joaquín de Olmedo *Ecuador*
Plácido *Cuba*
José Asunción Silva *Colombia*
Alfonsina Storni *Argentina*
Juan del Valle y Caviedes *Peru*

TRANSLATORS:
C. M. Lancaster, P. T. Manchester, Beatrice Gilman Proske, William Cullen
Bryant, Alice Stone Blackwell, Alfred Coester, Walter Owen, Mildred E.
Johnson, G. Dundas Craig, Alice Jane McVan.

26 *SPANISH STORIES; CUENTOS ESPAÑOLES**
Edited by Angel Flores
Anonymous translations (bilingual edition)
Bantam Books, New York, 1960. 339 pp. $0.95 (paper)

WRITERS:
Jorge Luis Borges *Argentina*
Benito Lynch *Argentina*

Ricardo Palma *Peru*
Horacio Quiroga *Uruguay*

This anthology also includes works by other writers.

27 *SPANISH STORIES AND TALES**
Edited by Harriet de Onís
Knopf, New York, 1954. 270 pp. $3.95

WRITERS:
Jorge Luis Borges *Argentina*
Arturo Cancela *Argentina*
Rómulo Gallegos *Venezuela*
Ricardo Güiraldes *Argentina*
Eduardo Mallea *Argentina*
Lino Novás Calvo *Cuba*

Ricardo Palma *Peru*
Horacio Quiroga *Uruguay*
Arturo Souto Alabarce *Mexico*
Benjamín Subercaseaux *Chile*
Hernando Téllez *Colombia*
Carlos Wyld Ospina *Guatemala*

24

TRANSLATORS:
Harriet de Onís, M. M. Lasley, Joan Coyne MacLean, Howard Young,
Raymond Sayers, John G. Underhill.

This anthology also includes stories by Spanish writers.

28 SWAN, CYGNETS, AND OWL; AN ANTHOLOGY OF MODERNIST POETRY IN SPANISH AMERICA*
Edited and translated by Mildred Edith Johnson (bilingual edition)
The University of Missouri Studies, Columbia, 1956. 199 pp. $4.00
(paper)

POETS:

Delmira Agustini *Uruguay*

Rafael Arévalo Martínez
  Guatemala

Rafael Alberto Arrieta *Argentina*

Enrique Banchs *Argentina*

Jorge Luis Borges *Argentina*

Julián del Casal *Cuba*

José Santos Chocano *Peru*

Rubén Darío *Nicaragua*

Enrique González Martínez
  Mexico

Manuel González Prada *Peru*

Manuel Gutiérrez Nájera *Mexico*

Julio Herrera y Reissig *Uruguay*

Juana de Ibarbourou *Uruguay*

Ricardo Jaimes Freyre *Bolivia*

Ramón López Velarde *Mexico*

Leopoldo Lugones *Argentina*

José Martí *Cuba*

Pablo Neruda *Chile*

Amado Nervo *Mexico*

José Asunción Silva *Colombia*

Alfonsina Storni *Argentina*

Jaime Torres Bodet *Mexico*

29 TALES FROM THE ARGENTINE*
Edited by Waldo Frank
Translated by Anita Brenner
Farrar & Rinehart, New York, 1930. 268 pp.

WRITERS:

Ricardo Güiraldes

Lucio Vicente López

Leopoldo Lugones

Roberto J. Payró

Horacio Quiroga *Uruguay*

Domingo Faustino Sarmiento

30 *THREE SPANISH AMERICAN POETS:*
PELLICER, NERUDA, ANDRADE*
Edited by Lloyd Mallan
Translated by Lloyd Mallan, Mary Wicker, C. V. Wicker, and
Joseph Leonard Grucci
Swallow & Critchlow, Albuquerque, 1942. 73 pp.

POETS:

Jorge Carrera Andrade   *Ecuador*
Pablo Neruda   *Chile*
Carlos Pellicer   *Mexico*

31 *THE TRIQUARTERLY ANTHOLOGY OF*
CONTEMPORARY LATIN AMERICAN LITERATURE
Edited by José Donoso and William Henkin
Dutton, New York, 1969. 496 pp. $8.95, $3.95 (paper)

WRITERS:

José Luis Appleyard   *Paraguay*
Homero Aridjis   *Mexico*
Juan José Arreola   *Mexico*
Miguel Arteche   *Chile*
Miguel Angel Asturias   *Guatemala*
Juan Bañuelos   *Mexico*
Rubén Bareiro Saguier   *Paraguay*
Miguel Barnet   *Cuba*
Efraín Barquero   *Chile*
Edgar Bayley   *Argentina*
Carlos Germán Belli   *Peru*
Jorge Luis Borges   *Argentina*
Miguel Angel Bustos   *Argentina*
Esteban Cabañas   *Paraguay*
César Calvo   *Peru*
Carlos Castro Saavedra   *Colombia*
Antonio Cisneros   *Peru*
Julio Cortázar   *Argentina*
René Dávalos   *Paraguay*
Washington Delgado   *Peru*
Eliseo Diego   *Cuba*
Ramiro Domínguez   *Paraguay*
José Donoso   *Chile*
Pablo Armando Fernández   *Cuba*
Roberto Fernández Retamar   *Cuba*

Adolfo Ferreiro   *Paraguay*
Isabel Fraire   *Mexico*
Carlos Fuentes   *Mexico*
Gabriel García Márquez   *Colombia*
Juan Gelman   *Argentina*
José María Gómez Sanjurjo
   Paraguay
Miguel Grinberg   *Argentina*
Oscar Hahn   *Chile*
Javier Heraud   *Peru*
Juan José Hernández   *Argentina*
Fayad Jamís   *Cuba*
Vicente Leñero   *Mexico*
José Lezama Lima   *Cuba*
Enrique Lihn   *Chile*
Clarice Lispector   *Brazil*
Leopoldo Marechal   *Argentina*
Carlos Martínez Moreno   *Uruguay*
Gonzalo Millán   *Chile*
Enrique Molina   *Argentina*
Sergio Mondragón   *Mexico*
Carlos J. Moneta   *Argentina*
Marco Antonio Montes de Oca
   Mexico
Pablo Neruda   *Chile*

Julio Ortega *Peru*
José Emilio Pacheco *Mexico*
Heberto Padilla *Cuba*
Basilia Papastamatíu *Argentina*
Nicanor Parra *Chile*
Octavio Paz *Mexico*
Francisco Pérez Maricevich
  Paraguay
Rafael Pineda *Venezuela*
Nélida Piñón *Brazil*
Gonzalo Rojas *Chile*
João Guimarães Rosa *Brazil*
Juan Gonzalo Rose *Peru*

Alberto Rubio *Chile*
Ernesto Sábato *Argentina*
Gustavo Sáinz *Mexico*
Horacio Salas *Argentina*
Joaquín Sanchez MacGregor
  Mexico
Máximo Simpson *Argentina*
Jorge Teillier *Chile*
Armando Tejada Gómez *Argentina*
Dalton Trevisan *Brazil*
César Vallejo *Peru*
Roque Vallejos *Paraguay*
Mario Vargas Llosa *Peru*

TRANSLATORS:
Clayton Eshleman, Stuart M. Gross, Paul Blackburn, John C. Murchison, Margaret Randall, Elinor Randall, Tim Reynolds, Gregory Rabassa, Stephen Berg, David Tipton, Maureen Ahern Maurer, J. S. Bernstein, Ronald Christ, Paschal Cantatore, Patrick Morgan, John Upton, Robert Bly, James Wright, Malcolm J. Parr, Ben Belitt, Lorraine O'Grady Freeman, William Witherup, Serge Echeverría, Miller Williams, Norman Thomas di Giovanni, John Hollander, Richard Howard, Cesar Rennert, W. S. Merwin, John Updike, Alastair Reid, Margaret S. Peden, Ameen Alwan, Agnes Moncy.

This anthology also includes essays by Octavio Paz, Emir Rodríguez Monegal, and Clayton Eshleman.

32 *TWELVE SPANISH AMERICAN POETS:*
    AN ANTHOLOGY*
Edited and translated by H. R. Hays (bilingual edition)
Yale University Press, New Haven, 1943. 336 pp.

POETS:
Jorge Luis Borges *Argentina*
Jorge Carrera Andrade *Ecuador*
Eugenio Florit *Cuba*
Jacinto Fombona Pachano
  Venezuela
José Gorostiza *Mexico*
Nicolás Guillén *Cuba*

Vicente Huidobro *Chile*
Luis Carlos López *Colombia*
Ramón López Velarde *Mexico*
Pablo Neruda *Chile*
Pablo de Rokha *Chile*
César Vallejo *Peru*

33 *WRITERS IN THE NEW CUBA*
Edited by J. M. Cohen
Penguin Books, Baltimore, 1967. 191 pp. $3.25

WRITERS:

Luis Agüero
Domingo Alfonso
José Alvarez Baragaño
Humberto Arenal
Antón Arrufat
Guillermo Cabrera Infante
Onelio Jorge Cardoso
Calvert Casey
Fidel Castro
Jesús Díaz Rodríguez
Abelardo Estorino

Pablo Armando Fernández
Roberto Fernández Retamar
Reynaldo González
Fayad Jamís
Rogelio Llopis
Luis Marré
Heberto Padilla
Virgilio Piñera
Rolando Rigali
Ana María Simo

TRANSLATORS:
J. G. Brotherston, J. M. Cohen, and Jean Franco.

II. Individual Works

1. POETRY

34 Andrade, Carlos Drummond de *Brazil*
IN THE MIDDLE OF THE ROAD: SELECTED POEMS
Edited and translated by John Nist (bilingual edition)
University of Arizona Press, Tucson, 1965. 121 pp. $4.75

35 Andrade, Mario de *Brazil*
HALLUCINATED CITY
Translated by Jack E. Tomlins (bilingual edition)
Vanderbilt University Press, Nashville, Tenn., 1968. 100 pp. $5.00
(original title: *Paulicea Desvairada*)

36 Carrera Andrade, Jorge *Ecuador*
TO THE BAY BRIDGE*
Translated by Eleanor L. Turnbull (bilingual edition)
Stanford University Press, Stanford, 1941. 20 pp.
(original title: *Canto al Puente de Oakland*)

37 Carrera Andrade, Jorge
*SECRET COUNTRY**
Translated by Muna Lee (bilingual edition)
Macmillan, New York, 1946. 77 pp.
(original title: *País secreto*)

38 Chocano, José Santos   *Peru*
*SPIRIT OF THE ANDES**
Translated by E. W. Underwood
Mosher Press, Portland, 1935. 43 pp.
(selection of poetry)

39 Darío, Rubén   *Nicaragua*
*ELEVEN POEMS OF RUBÉN DARÍO**
Translated by Thomas Walsh and Salomón de la Selva (bilingual edition)
Putnam, New York, 1916. 46 pp.
(selection of poems including *Primaveral, Canto de esperanza, Canción de otoño en primavera*, and others)

40 Darío, Rubén
*PROSAS PROFANAS AND OTHER POEMS**
Translated by Charles B. McMichael
Nicholas L. Brown, New York, 1922. 60 pp.
(selection of poetry from *Prosas profanas* and other works)

41 Darío, Rubén
SELECTED POEMS OF RUBÉN DARÍO
Prologue by Octavio Paz; translated by Lysander Kemp
University of Texas Press, Austin, 1965. 149 pp. $4.50
(selection of poetry from *Rimas, Azul, Prosas Profanas*, and other works)

42 Ercilla y Zúñiga, Alonso de   *Chile*
*THE ARAUCANIAD**
Translated by C. M. Lancaster and P. T. Manchester
Vanderbilt University Press, Nashville, 1945. 326 pp.
(original title: *La Araucana*)

42a Giraudier, Antonio *Cuba*
GREEN AGAINST LINEN, AND OTHER POEMS*
Translated by Antonio Giraudier and Samuel Weisberg (bilingual
   edition)
Bookman Associates, New York, 1957. 89 pp.
(selections of poems)

43 Gorostiza, José *Mexico*
DEATH WITHOUT END
Translated by Laura Villaseñor (bilingual edition)
University of Texas Press (Humanities Research Center), Austin,
   1969. 40 pp. . $10.00
(original title: *Muerte sin fin*)

44 Guillén, Nicolás *Cuba*
CUBA LIBRE: POEMS*
Translated by Langston Hughes and Ben Frederic Carruthers
The Ward Ritchie Press, Los Angeles, 1948. 98 pp.
(selections from *El son entero*)

45 Hernández, José *Argentina*
THE GAUCHO MARTÍN FIERRO
Translated by C. E. Ward (bilingual edition)
State University of New York Press, Albany, 1967. xvii, 507 pp.
   $10.00
(original title: *Martín Fierro*)

46 Juana Inés de la Cruz, Sor (pseud. of Juana de Asbaje)
   Mexico
THE PATHLESS GROVE: SONNETS*
Translated by Pauline Cook
Decker Press, Prairie City, 1950. 53 pp.
(selection of poetry)

47 Lima, Jorge de *Brazil*
BRAZILIAN PSALM*
Translated by Willis Wager
G. Schirmer, New York, 1941. 24 pp.
(original title: *Salmo*)

30

48 Mistral, Gabriela *Chile*
SELECTED POEMS OF GABRIELA MISTRAL
Translated by Langston Hughes
Indiana University Press, Bloomington, 1957. 119 pp. $3.50, $1.75
    (paper)
(selection of poetry from *Tala, Ternura, Poemas de las Madres* and
    other works)

49 Neruda, Pablo *Chile*
SELECTED POEMS BY PABLO NERUDA*
Translated by Angel Flores
Privately printed, 1944. 26 pp.
(selection of poems)

50 Neruda, Pablo
RESIDENCE ON EARTH AND OTHER POEMS*
Translated by Angel Flores (bilingual edition)
New Directions, Norfolk, 1946. 205 pp.
(selection from *Residencia en la tierra, Canto general,* and other works)

51 Neruda, Pablo
THREE MATERIAL SONGS*
Translated by Angel Flores
East River Editions, New York, 1948. 31 pp.
(original title: *Tres cantos materiales* from *Residencia II*)

52 Neruda, Pablo
SELECTED POEMS*
Edited and translated by Ben Belitt (bilingual edition)
Grove Press, New York, 1961, 321 pp.
(selection from *Residencia en la tierra, Canto general, Odas elementales,*
    and other works)

53 Neruda, Pablo
ELEMENTARY ODES
Translated by Carlos Lozano (bilingual edition)
Las Americas, New York, 1961. 155 pp. $4.00
(original title: *Odas elementales*)

54 Neruda, Pablo
RESIDENCE ON EARTH*
Translated by Clayton Eshleman
Amber House Press, San Francisco, 1962. Unpaged.
(selections from *Residencia en la tierra*)

55 Neruda, Pablo
BESTIARY
Translated by E. Newberger (bilingual edition)
Harcourt, Brace and World, New York, 1965. 40 pp. $12.50
(original title: *Bestiario*)

56 Neruda, Pablo
TWENTY POEMS OF PABLO NERUDA
Translated by James Wright and Robert Bly (bilingual edition)
Sixties Press, Madison, Minnesota, 1967. $2.00, $1.00 (paper)
(poems from *Residencia en la tierra*, *Canto general*, *Odas elementales*)

57 Neruda, Pablo
THE HEIGHTS OF MACCHU PICCHU
Translated by Nathaniel Tarn (bilingual edition)
Farrar, Straus and Giroux, New York, 1967. 71 pp. $4.50
Noonday, New York, 1967. $1.95 (paper)
(original title: *Alturas de Macchu Picchu*)

58 Neruda, Pablo
WE ARE MANY
Translated by Alastair Reid (bilingual edition)
Grossman, New York, 1968. 28 pp. $4.00, $2.50 (paper)
(selection of poetry from *Estravagario* and other works)

59 Neruda, Pablo
PABLO NERUDA: A NEW DECADE (POEMS: 1958–1967)
Translated by Ben Belitt and Alastair Reid
Grove Press, New York, 1969. 274 pp. $8.50
(selection of latest poetry)

60 Neruda, Pablo
THE EARLY POEMS
Translated by David Ossman and Carlos B. Hagen
New Rivers Press, New York, 1969. 100 pp. $3.75
(selection of poems from *Crepusculario*, *Veinte poemas de amor y una
canción desesperada*, *Anillos*, and other works)

61 Nervo, Amado *Mexico*
*PLENITUDE**
Translated by William F. Rice (bilingual edition)
J. R. Miller, Los Angeles, 1928. 153 pp.
(original title: *Plenitud*)

62 Nervo, Amado
CONFESSIONS OF A MODERN POET*
Translated by Dorothy Kress
Bruce Humphries, Boston, 1935. 50 pp.
(Prose piece with selection of poetry)

63 Novo, Salvador Mexico
NUEVO AMOR*
Translated by E. W. Underwood
Mosher Press, Portland, 1935. 52 pp.
(selection of poetry from Nuevo amor and other works)

64 Oña, Pedro de Chile
ARAUCO TAMED*
Translated by Charles Maxwell Lancaster and Paul Thomas
    Manchester
University of New Mexico Press, Albuquerque, 1948. 283 pp.
(original title: Arauco domado)

65 Ortiz Vargas, Alfredo Colombia
THE TOWERS OF MANHATTAN; A SPANISH
    AMERICAN POET LOOKS AT NEW YORK*
Translated by Quincy Guy Burris
University of New Mexico Press, Albuquerque, 1944. 137 pp.
(original title: Las torres de Manhattan)

66 Parra, Nicanor Chile
ANTI-POEMS*
Translated by Jorge Elliott
City Lights Books, San Francisco, 1960. 32 pp.
(selections from Poemas y Antipoemas)

67 Parra, Nicanor
POEMS AND ANTIPOEMS. POEMAS Y ANTIPOEMAS
Translated by Miller Williams, W. S. Merwin, Allen Ginsberg,
    William Carlos Williams, and others (bilingual edition)
New Directions, New York, 1967. 160 pp. $5.50, $1.95 (paper)
(selection of poetry from Poemas y Antipoemas, Versos de salón, Can-
    ciones rusas, and Ejercicios respiratorios)

68 Paz, Octavio *Mexico*
*SELECTED POEMS OF OCTAVIO PAZ**
Translated by Muriel Rukeyser (bilingual edition)
Indiana University Press, Bloomington, 1963. 171 pp. $5.95
(selection of poetry from *Libertad bajo palabra, Condición de nube, El girasol*, and other works)

68a Paz, Octavio
*SUN STONE**
Translated by Muriel Rukeyser (bilingual edition)
New Directions, New York, 1963. 47 pp. $1.00 (paper)
(original title: *Piedra de sol*)

69 Porchia, Antonio *Argentina*
VOICES
Translated by W. S. Merwin
Follett, (Big Table Publishing Paperback), Chicago, 1969. 64 pp.
   $2.95
(original title: *Voces*)

70 Torres Bodet, Jaime *Mexico*
SELECTED POEMS OF JAIME TORRES BODET
Translated by Sonja Karsen (bilingual edition)
Indiana University Press, Bloomington, 1964. 155 pp. $5.75
(selection of poetry from *Fervor, Canciones, El corazón delirante* and
   other works)

71 Torri, Julio *Mexico*
*JULIO TORRI: ESSAYS AND POEMS**
Translated by Dorothy Kress
Publications of French Studies, New York, 1938. 35 pp.
(selections of essays and poems)

72 Vallejo, César *Peru*
*TWENTY POEMS OF CESAR VALLEJO**
Translated by John Knoepfle, James Wright and Robert Bly (bi-
   lingual edition)
Sixties Press, Madison, Minnesota, 1967. 63 pp.
(selection of poetry)

73 Vallejo, César
POEMAS HUMANOS, HUMAN POEMS
Translated by Clayton Eshleman
Grove Press, New York, 1968. 326 pp. $8.50, 1969, $2.95 (paper)
(original title: *Poemas humanos*)

73a Zorrilla de San Martín, Juan *Uruguay*
*TABARE**
Translated by Walter Owen and Frank P. Hebblewaite (bilingual
    edition)
Pan American Union, Washington, 1956. 366 pp. $3.75
(original title: *Tabaré*)

2. FICTION

A. SHORT STORIES

74 Amado, Jorge *Brazil*
THE TWO DEATHS OF QUINCAS WATERYELL
Translated by Barbara Shelby
Knopf, New York, 1965. 112 pp. $3.95
(original title: *A Morte e a morte de Quincas Berro D'agua*, from the
    book *Os velhos marinheiros: Duas histórias do cais da Bahia*)

74a Anderson-Imbert, Enrique *Argentina*
THE OTHER SIDE OF THE MIRROR
Translated by Isabel Reade
Southern Illinois University Press, Carbondale, 1966. 248 pp. $5.95
(original title: *El grimorio*)

75 Arreola, Juan José *Mexico*
CONFABULARIO AND OTHER INVENTIONS
Translated by George D. Schade
University of Texas Press, Austin, 1964. 245 pp. $5.00
(original title: *Confabulario*)

76 Borges, Jorge Luis *Argentina*
LABYRINTHS: SELECTED STORIES AND OTHER
    WRITINGS
Edited by Donald A. Yates and James E. Irby
Translated by the editors, Anthony Kerrigan, Harriet de Onís, and
    others
New Directions, New York, 1961. 260 pp. $5.50, 1964, $1.95 (paper)
(stories from *El Aleph* and *Ficciones*, parables from *El hacedor*, essays
    from *Otras inquisiciones* and *Discusión*)

77 Borges, Jorge Luis
FICCIONES
Edited by Anthony Kerrigan
Translated by Anthony Kerrigan, Alastair Reid, and others
Grove Press, New York, 1962. 174 pp. $3.50; 1963, $2.45 (paper)
(original title: *Ficciones*)

78 Borges, Jorge Luis
DREAMTIGERS
Translated by Mildred Boyer and Harold Morland
University of Texas Press, Austin, 1964. 95 pp. $4.00
(original title: *El hacedor*)

79 Borges, Jorge Luis
A PERSONAL ANTHOLOGY
Edited by Anthony Kerrigan
Translated by Anthony Kerrigan, Alastair Reid, and others
Grove Press, New York, 1967. 210 pp. $5.00; 1968, $1.95 (paper)
(original title: *Antología personal*, a collection of poems, short stories
    and essays)

80 Borges, Jorge Luis
THE BOOK OF IMAGINARY BEINGS
Translated by Norman Thomas di Giovanni
Dutton, New York, 1969. 256 pp. $6.95
(original title: *El libro de los seres imaginarios*)

81 Cortázar, Julio *Argentina*
END OF THE GAME AND OTHER STORIES
Translated by Paul Blackburn
Pantheon, New York, 1967. 277 pp. $4.95
Paperback: (BLOW-UP), Collier Books, New York, 1968. 277 pp.
    $1.50
(stories from *Bestiario*, *Las armas secretas*, and *Final del juego*)

82 Cortázar, Julio
CRONOPIOS AND FAMAS
Translated by Paul Blackburn
Pantheon, New York, 1969. 161 pp. $4.95
(original title: *Historias de cronopios y famas*)

83 García Márquez, Gabriel *Colombia*
NO ONE WRITES TO THE COLONEL AND OTHER
  STORIES
Translated by J. S. Bernstein
Harper and Row, New York, 1968. 170 pp. $5.95
(original title: *El coronel no tiene quien le escriba* and *Los funerales de la
  Mamá Grande*)

84 Gerchunoff, Alberto *Argentina*
THE JEWISH GAUCHOS OF THE PAMPAS*
Translated by Prudencio de Pereda
Abelar-Schuman, New York, 1955 and 1959. 169 pp.
(original title: *Los gauchos judíos*)

85 Lillo, Baldomero *Chile*
THE DEVIL'S PIT AND OTHER STORIES*
Translated by Esther S. Dillon and Angel Flores
Pan American Union, Washington, 1959. 152 pp.
(collection of short stories from the works *Sub Terra*; *Cuadros mineros*,
  Sub Sole, and *Relatos populares*)

86 Lobato, Monteiro *Brazil*
BRAZILIAN SHORT STORIES*
Anonymous translation
Haldeman-Julius, Girard, 1925. 64 pp. (Little Blue Book no. 733)
(three stories by the author)

87 Machado de Assis, Joaquim María *Brazil*
THE PSYCHIATRIST AND OTHER STORIES
Translated by William L. Grossman and Helen Caldwell
University of California Press, Berkeley, 1963. 147 pp. $5.00, $1.95
  (paper)
(selection from the book *Papéis avulsos* and other works)

88 Martínez Cáceres, Arturo *Mexico*
IN MEMORIAM: MEXICAN SHORT STORIES
Translated by D. O. Chambers
Vantage Press, New York, 1967. 117 pp. $2.95
(a selection of the author's stories)

89 Palma, Ricardo *Peru*
*THE KNIGHTS OF THE CAPE AND THIRTY-SEVEN
OTHER SELECTIONS FROM THE "TRADICIONES
PERUANAS"**
Translated by Harriet de Onís
Knopf, New York, 1945. 246 pp.
(selections from *Tradiciones peruanas*)

90 Quiroga, Horacio *Uruguay*
SOUTH AMERICAN JUNGLE TALES*
Translated by Arthur Livingston
Duffield and Co., New York, 1922. 166 pp.; Dodd, Mead, New
     York, 1940
(original title: *Cuentos de la selva*)

91 Rosa, João Guimarães *Brazil*
SAGARANA
Translated by Harriet de Onís
Knopf, New York, 1966. 303 pp. $5.95
(original title: *Sagarana*)

92 Rosa, João Guimarães
THE THIRD BANK OF THE RIVER
Translated by Barbara Shelby
Knopf, New York, 1968. 256 pp. $5.95
(original title: *Primeiras estorias*)

93 Rulfo, Juan *Mexico*
THE BURNING PLAIN AND OTHER STORIES
Translated by George D. Schade
University of Texas Press, 1967. 195 pp. $5.00
(original title: *El llano en llamas*)

94 Subercaseaux, Benjamín *Chile*
FROM WEST TO EAST: FIVE STORIES*
Translated by John Garrett Underhill
Putnam, New York, 1940. 215 pp.
(original titles: *Y al oeste limita con el mar* and *Rahab*)

38

B. NOVELS

94a Aguilera-Malta, Demetrio *Ecuador*
MANUELA LA CABALLERESA DEL SOL
Translated by Willis Knapp Jones
Southern Illinois University Press, Carbondale, 1967. 320 pp. $6.95
(original title: *Manuela la caballeresa del sol*)

95 Alegría, Ciro *Peru*
*BROAD AND ALIEN IS THE WORLD**
Translated by Harriet de Onís
Holt, Rinehart and Winston, New York, 1963. 434 pp.
(original title: *El mundo es ancho y ajeno*)

96 Alegría, Ciro
GOLDEN SERPENT
Translated by Harriet de Onís
Signet, New York, 1963. 192 pp. $0.60 (paper)
(original title: *La serpiente de oro*)

97 Alegría, Fernando *Chile*
*LAUTARO**
Translated by Delia Goetz
Farrar and Rinehart, New York, 1944. 176 pp.
(original title: *Lautaro, joven libertador de Arauco*)

98 Alegría, Fernando
MY HORSE GONZALEZ
Translated by Carlos Lozano
Las Americas, New York, 1964. 187 pp. $4.00
(original title: *Caballo de copas*)

99 Almeida, Manuel Antônio de *Brazil*
*MEMOIRS OF A MILITIA SERGEANT**
Translated by Linton L. Barrett
Pan American Union, Washington D.C., 1959. 244 pp.
(original title: *Memórias de um sargento de milicias*)

100 Altamirano, Ignacio M. *Mexico*
CHRISTMAS IN THE MOUNTAINS*
Translated by Harvey L. Johnson
University of Florida Press, 1961. 68 pp.
(original title: *La Navidad en las montañas*)

101 Amado, Jorge *Brazil*
GABRIELA, CLOVE AND CINNAMON
Translated by James L. Taylor and William L. Grossman
Knopf, New York, 1962. 480 pp. $5.95. Fawcett, Greenwich, 1969.
  400 pp. $0.75 (paper)
(original title: *Gabriela, cravo e canela*)

102 Amado, Jorge
HOME IS THE SAILOR
Translated by Harriet de Onís
Knopf, New York, 1964. 320 pp. $4.95
(original title: *Capitães de areia*)

103 Amado, Jorge
VIOLENT LAND
Translated by Samuel Putnam
Knopf, New York, 1965. 352 pp. $5.95
(original title: *Terras do sem fim*)

104 Amado, Jorge
THE SHEPHERDS OF THE NIGHT
Translated by Harriet de Onís
Knopf, New York, 1967. 364 pp. $5.95
(original title: *Os pastores da noite*)

105 Amado, Jorge
DONA FLOR AND HER TWO HUSBANDS
Translated by Harriet de Onís
Knopf, New York, 1969. 576 pp. $6.95
(original title: *Dona Flor e seus dois maridos*)

106 Amorim, Enrique *Uruguay*
THE HORSE AND HIS SHADOW*
Translated by Lt. Richard L. O'Connell and James Graham Luján
Scribners, New York, 1943. 252 pp.
(original title: *El caballo y su sombra*)

107 Andrade, Mario de *Brazil*
FRÄULEIN*
Translated by Margaret Richardson Hollingworth
Macaulay, New York, 1933. 252 pp.
(original title: *Amar, verbo intransitivo*)

108 Aranha, José Pereira de Graça *Brazil*
CANAAN*
Translated by Mariano Joaquín Lorente
The Four Seas Company, Boston, 1920. 321 pp.
(original title: *Chanaan*)

109 Arcocha, Juan *Cuba*
A CANDLE IN THE WIND
Anonymous translation
Lyle Stuart, New York, 1967. 187 pp. $4.00
(original title not available)

109a Arenal, Humberto *Cuba*
THE SUN BEATS DOWN*
Translated by Joseph M. Bernstein
Hill and Wang, New York, 1959. 96 pp. $1.50
(original title not available)

110 Asturias, Miguel Angel *Guatemala*
EL SEÑOR PRESIDENTE
Translated by Frances Partridge
Atheneum, New York, 1964. 288 pp. $4.50
(original title: *El señor presidente*)

111 Asturias, Miguel Angel
MULATA
Translated by Gregory Rabassa
Delacorte Press, New York, 1967. 307 pp. $7.95, $0.95 (paper)
(original title: *Mulata de tal*)

112 Asturias, Miguel Angel
STRONG WIND
Translated by Gregory Rabassa
Delacorte Press, New York, 1968. 242 pp. $7.95
(original title: *Viento fuerte*)

112a Ayala, Robert H. *Guatemala*
*QUARTER TO SIX**
Translated by Emil G. Beavers
Exposition Press, New York, 1955. 186 pp. $3.50
(original title not available)

113 Azevedo, Aluizio *Brazil*
*A BRAZILIAN TENEMENT**
Translated by Harry W. Brown
R. M. McBride & Co., New York, 1926. 320 pp.
(original title: *O cortiço*)

114 Azuela, Mariano *Mexico*
*MARCELA, A MEXICAN LOVE STORY**
Translated by Anita Brenner
Farrar and Rinehart, New York, 1932. 244 pp.
(original title: *Mala yerba*)

115 Azuela, Mariano
UNDERDOGS
Translated by E. Munguía, Jr.
New American Library (Signet), New York, 1963. 149 pp. $0.75
   (paper)
(original title: *Los de abajo*)

116 Azuela, Mariano
TRIALS OF A RESPECTABLE FAMILY
   AND THE UNDERDOGS
Translated by F. K. Hendricks
Trinity University Press, San Antonio, 1963. 267 pp. $6.00
(original title: *Las tribulaciones de una familia decente* and *Los de abajo*)

117 Azuela, Mariano
TWO NOVELS OF MEXICO: THE FLIES, THE BOSSES
Translated by Lesley Byrd Simpson
University of California Press, Berkeley, 1965. 194 pp. $1.25 (paper)
(original titles: *Las moscas, Los caciques*)

118 Barrios, Eduardo *Chile*
BROTHER ASNO
Translated by Edmundo García Girón
Las Americas, New York, 1969. 184 pp. $3.50
(original title: *El hermano asno*)

119 Benedetti, Mario *Uruguay*
THE TRUCE
Translated by Benjamin Graham
Harper and Row, New York, 1969. 184 pp. $5.00
(original title: *La tregua*)

120 Bioy Casares, Adolfo *Argentina*
THE INVENTION OF MOREL AND OTHER STORIES
Translated by Ruth L. C. Simms
University of Texas Press, Austin, 1964. 237 pp. $5.00
(original title: *La invención de Morel* and stories from *La trama celeste*)

121 Blanco Fombona, Rufino *Venezuela*
THE MAN OF GOLD*
Translated by Isaac Goldberg
Brentano's, New York, 1920. 319 pp.
(original title: *El hombre de oro*)

122 Blest Gana, Alberto *Chile*
MARTÍN RIVAS*
Translated by Mrs. Charles Whitham
Knopf, New York, 1918. 437 pp. $1.60
(original title: *Martín Rivas*)

123 Bombal, María Luisa *Chile*
THE SHROUDED WOMAN*
Anonymous translation
Farrar and Straus, New York, 1948. 198 pp.
(original title: *La amortajada*)

123a   Bombal, María Luisa
*THE HOUSE OF MIST**
Anonymous translation
Farrar, Straus, New York, 1946. 245 pp.
(original title: *La última niebla*)

124   Carballido, Emilio   *Mexico*
THE NORTHER
Translated by Margaret Sayers Peden
University of Texas Press, Austin, 1968. 101 pp. $3.50
(original title: *El norte*)

125   Carneiro, Cecilio J.   *Brazil*
*THE BONFIRE**
Translated by Dudley Poore
Farrar and Rinehart, New York, 1944. 334 pp.
(original title: *A fogueira*)

126   Carpentier, Alejo
THE LOST STEPS
Translated by Harriet de Onís
Knopf, New York, 1956 and 1967. 304 pp. $5.95
(original title: *Los pasos perdidos*)

127   Carpentier, Alejo   *Cuba*
*THE KINGDOM OF THIS WORLD**
Translated by Harriet de Onís
Knopf, New York, 1957. 150 pp. $3.00
(original title: *El reino de este mundo*)

128   Carpentier, Alejo
*EXPLOSION IN A CATHEDRAL**
Translated by John Sturrock
Little, Brown and Co., Boston, 1963. 351 pp.
(original title: *El siglo de las luces*)

129   Castellanos Rosario   *Mexico*
NINE GUARDIANS
Translated by Irene Nicholson
Vanguard, New York, 1959. 272 pp. $3.95
(original title: *Balún—Canán*)

130 Corção, Gustavo *Brazil*
WHO IF I CRY OUT
Translated by Clotilde Wilson
University of Texas Press, Austin, 1967. 218 pp. $6.00
(original title: *Liçoes de abismo*)

131 Cortázar, Julio *Argentina*
*THE WINNERS**
Translated by E. Kerrigan
Pantheon, New York, 1965. 374 pp. $5.95
(original title: *Los premios*)

132 Cortázar, Julio
HOPSCOTCH
Translated by Gregory Rabassa
Pantheon, New York, 1966. 564 pp. $6.95
The New American Library (Signet), New York, 1967. 448 pp. $0.95
   (paper)
(original title: *Rayuela*)

133 Costa du Rels, Adolfo *Bolivia*
*BEWITCHED LANDS**
Translated by Stuart Grummon
Knopf, New York, 1945. 224 pp. $2.50
(original title: *Tierras hechizadas*)

134 Denevi, Marco *Argentina*
*ROSA AT 10 O'CLOCK**
Translated by Donald A. Yates
Holt, Rinehart & Winston, New York, 1964. 191 pp.
(original title: *Rosaura a las diez*)

135 Díaz Sánchez, Ramón *Venezuela*
CUMBOTO
Translated by John Upton
University of Texas Press, Austin, 1969. 273 pp. $6.50
(original title: *Cumboto*)

45

136   Donoso, José   *Chile*
CORONATION
Translated by Jocasta Goodwin
Knopf, New York, 1965. 288 pp. $4.95
(original title: *Coronación*)

137   Donoso, José
THIS SUNDAY
Translated by Lorraine O'Grady
Knopf, New York, 1967. 224 pp. $4.95
(original title: *Este domingo*)

138   Dourado, Autran   *Brazil*
A HIDDEN LIFE
Translated by Edgar Miller, Jr.
Knopf, New York, 1969. 160 pp. $4.50
(original title: *Uma vida em silencio*)

139   Echeverría, Esteban   *Argentina*
THE SLAUGHTER-HOUSE
Translated by Angel Flores
Las Americas, New York, 1959. 37 pp. $1.00 (paper)
(original title: *El matadero*)

140   Filho, Adonias   *Brazil*
MEMORIES OF LAZARUS
Translated by Fred P. Ellison
University of Texas Press, Austin, 1969. 170 pp. $5.00
(original title: *Memórias de Lázaro*)

140a   Fonseca, Rodolfo L.   *Uruguay*
*TOWER OF IVORY**
Translated by Walter Starkie
J. Messner, New York, 1954. 279 pp.
(original title: *Turris ebúrnea*)

141   Freyre, Gilberto   *Brazil*
MOTHER AND SON: A BRAZILIAN TALE
Translated by Barbara Shelby
Knopf, New York, 1967. 224 pp. $4.95
(original title: *Dona Sinhá e o filho padre*)

142   Fuentes, Carlos   *Mexico*
WHERE THE AIR IS CLEAR
Translated by Sam Hileman
Farrar, Straus & Giroux, New York, 1960. 376 pp. $4.95
(original title: *La región más transparente*)

143   Fuentes, Carlos
THE GOOD CONSCIENCE
Anonymous translation
Farrar, Straus & Giroux, New York, 1961. 148 pp. $3.95, $1.95
   (paper)
(original title: *Las buenas conciencias*)

144   Fuentes, Carlos
THE DEATH OF ARTEMIO CRUZ
Translated by Sam Hileman
Farrar, Straus & Giroux, New York, 1964. 306 pp. $4.95; 1966,
   $1.95 (paper)
(original title: *La muerte de Artemio Cruz*)

145   Fuentes, Carlos
AURA
Translated by Lysander Kemp
Farrar, Straus & Giroux, New York, 1966. 74 pp. $3.95
(original title: *Aura*)

146   Fuentes, Carlos
A CHANGE OF SKIN
Translated by Sam Hileman
Farrar, Straus & Giroux, 1968. 462 pp. $6.95
(original title: *Cambio de piel*)

147   Galindo, Sergio   *Mexico*
THE PRECIPICE
Translated by John and Carolyn Brushwood
University of Texas Press, Austin, 1969. 185 pp. $6.00
(original title: *El bordo*)

148 Gallegos, Rómulo *Venezuela*
DOÑA BARBARA
Translated by Robert Malloy
Peter Smith, New York, 1948. 440 pp. $4.00
(original title: *Doña Bárbara*)

149 Galván, Manuel de Jesús *Dominican Republic*
*THE CROSS AND THE SWORD**
Translated by Robert Graves
Indiana University Press, Bloomington, 1954. 366 pp.
(original title: *Enriquillo, leyenda histórica dominicana*)

150 Gálvez, Manuel *Argentina*
*NACHA REGULES**
Translated by Leo Ongley
Dutton, New York, 1922. 304 pp.
(original title: *Nacha Regules*)

151 Gálvez, Manuel
*HOLY WEDNESDAY**
Translated by Warre B. Wells
Appleton, New York, 1934. 208 pp.
(original title: *Miércoles santo*)

152 Garro, Elena *Mexico*
RECOLLECTIONS OF THINGS TO COME
Translated by Ruth L. C. Simms
University of Texas Press, Austin, 1969. 289 pp. $6.50
(original title: *Los recuerdos del porvenir*)

153 Gil Gilbert, Enrique *Ecuador*
*OUR DAILY BREAD**
Translated by Dudley Poore
Farrar & Rinehart, New York, 1943. 246 pp.
(original title: *Nuestro pan*)

154 Guido, Beatriz *Argentina*
*THE HOUSE OF THE ANGEL**
Translated by Joan C. MacLean
McGraw-Hill, New York, 1957. 174 pp.
(original title: *La casa del ángel*)

155 Guido, Beatriz
END OF A DAY*
Translated by A. D. Towers
Scribner, New York, 1966. 278 pp. $4.95
(original title: *El incendio y las vísperas*)

156 Güiraldes, Ricardo *Argentina*
DON SEGUNDO SOMBRA
Translated by Harriet de Onís
New American Library (Signet), New York, 1966. 222 pp. $0.75
   (paper)
(original title: *Don Segundo Sombra*)

157 Guzmán, Martín L. *Mexico*
THE EAGLE AND THE SERPENT
Translated by Harriet de Onís
Peter Smith, Gloucester, 1969. 386 pp. $3.50
(original title: *El águila y la serpiente*)

158 Guzmán, Martín L.
MEMOIRS OF PANCHO VILLA
Translated by V. Taylor
University of Texas Press, Austin, 1965. 512 pp. $8.50
(original title: *Las memorias de Pancho Villa*)

159 Huidobro, Vicente *Chile*
MIRROR OF A MAGE*
Translated by Warre B. Wells
Houghton Mifflin, Boston, 1931. 185 pp.
(original title: *Cagliostro*)

160 Huidobro, Vicente
PORTRAIT OF A PALADIN*
Translated by Warre B. Wells
Horace Liveright, New York, 1932. 315 pp.
(original title: *Mio Cid Campeador*)

161 Icaza, Jorge *Ecuador*
THE VILLAGERS
Translated by Bernard Dulsey
Southern Illinois University Press, Carbondale, Illinois, 1964. 223 pp.
$5.95
(original title: *Huasipungo*)

162 Isaacs, Jorge *Colombia*
*MARÍA, A SOUTH AMERICAN ROMANCE**
Translated by Rollo Ogden
Harpers, New York, 1890 and 1918. 302 pp.
(original title: *María*)

163 Lafourcade, Enrique *Chile*
*KING AHAB'S FEAST**
Translated by Renate and Ray Morrison
St. Martin's Press, New York, 1963. 249 pp.
(original title: *La fiesta del rey Acab*)

164 Larreta, Enrique *Argentina*
*THE GLORY OF DON RAMIRO**
Translated by L. B. Walton
Dutton, New York, 1924. 307 pp.
(original title: *La gloria de Don Ramiro*)

165 Lispector, Clarice *Brazil*
THE APPLE IN THE DARK
Translated by Gregory Rabassa
Knopf, New York, 1967. 384 pp. $5.95
(original title: *A maçâ no escuro*)

166 López y Fuentes, Gregorio *Mexico*
EL INDIO
Translated by Anita Brenner
Ungar, New York, 1961. 256 pp. $5.00
(original title: *El indio*)

167 Machado de Assis, Joaquím María *Brazil*
*DON CASMURRO**
Translated by Helen Caldwell
Farrar, Straus & Giroux, Noonday, 1953. 283 pp.
(original title: *Don Casmurro*)

168 Machado de Assis, Joaquím María
*PHILOSOPHER OR DOG?**
Translated by Clotilde Wilson
Farrar, Straus & Giroux, 1954. 271 pp.
(original title: *Quincas Borba*)

169 Machado de Assis, Joaquím María
ESAU AND JACOB
Translated by H. Caldwell
University of California Press, Berkeley, 1966. 269 pp. $5.50, $1.50
    (paper)
(original title: *Esaú e Jacob*)

170 Machado de Assis, Joaquím María
DON CASMURRO
Translated by Helen Caldwell
University of California Press, Berkeley, 1966. 269 pp. $5.50, $1.50
    (paper)
(original title: *Don Casmurro*)

171 Machado de Assis, Joaquím María
EPITAPH OF A SMALL WINNER
Translated by William L. Grossman
Farrar, Straus & Giroux, 1967. 223 pp. $5.50, Noonday, $1.50 (paper)
(original title: *Memórias póstumas de Bras Cubas*)

172 Magdaleno, Mauricio *Mexico*
*SUNBURST**
Translated by Anita Brenner
Viking Press, New York, 1944. 290 pp.
(original title: *El resplandor*)

173 Mallea, Eduardo *Argentina*
THE BAY OF SILENCE*
Translated by Stuart E. Grummon
Knopf, New York, 1944. 352 pp. $2.50
(original title: *La bahía de silencio*)

174 Mallea, Eduardo
ALL GREEN SHALL PERISH
Edited by John B. Hughes
Translated by John B. Hughes, Harriet de Onís, and others
Knopf, New York, 1966. 431 pp. $7.95
(original title: *Todo verdor perecerá* and a selection of novels and
  stories)

175 Mármol, José *Argentina*
AMALIA: A ROMANCE OF THE ARGENTINE*
Translated by Mary J. Serrano
Dutton, New York, 1919. 419 pp.
(original title: *Amalia*)

176 Marroquin, Lorenzo *Colombia*
PAX (PEACE)*
Translated by Isaac Goldberg and W. V. Schierbrand
Brentano, New York, 1920. 480 pp.
(original title: *Pax, novela de costumbres latino-americanas*)

177 Menéndez, Miguel Angel *Mexico*
NAYAR*
Translated by Angel Flores
Farrar and Rinehart, New York, 1942. 277 pp.
(original title: *Nayar*)

178 Mondragón Aguirre, Magdalena *Mexico*
SOME DAY THE DREAM*
Translated by Samuel Putnam
Dial Press, New York, 1947. 240 pp.
(original title: *Yo como pobre*)

179 Mujica-Láinez, Manuel *Argentina*
BOMARZO
Translated by Gregory Rabassa
Simon & Schuster, New York, 1969. 573 pp. $8.95
(original title: *Bomarzo*)

180 Onetti, Juan Carlos *Uruguay*
THE SHIPYARD
Translated by Rachel Caffyn
Scribners, New York, 1968. 190 pp. $4.95
(original title: *El astillero*)

181 Parra, Teresa de la *Venezuela*
*MÁMA BLANCA'S SOUVENIRS**
Translated by Harriet de Onís
Pan American Union, Washington, D.C., 1950. 129 pp.
(original title: *Memorias de Mamá Blanca*)

182 Petit, Magdalena *Chile*
*LA QUINTRALA**
Translated by Lulú Vargas Vila
Macmillan, New York, 1942. 190 pp.
(original title: *La Quintrala*)

183 Prado, Pedro *Chile*
COUNTRY JUDGE
Translated by Lesley Simpson Byrd
University of California Press, Berkeley, 1967. 143 pp. $4.95
(original title: *Un juez rural*)

184 Prato, Luis F. *Venezuela*
*WIND STORM: A NOVEL OF THE VENEZUELAN
   ANDES*
Translated by Hugh Jencks
Las Americas, New York, 1961. 221 pp. $3.50
(original title: *Ventisca*)

185   Queiroz, Rachel de   *Brazil*
THE THREE MARIAS*
Translated by Fred P. Ellison
University of Texas Press, Austin, 1963. 178 pp. $4.00
(original title: *As três Marias*)

186   **Ramos, Graciliano**   *Brazil*
ANGUISH*
Translated by L. C. Kaplan
Knopf, New York, 1946. 256 pp. $2.50
(original title: *Angústia*)

187   **Ramos, Graciliano**
BARREN LIVES
Translated by Ralph E. Dimmick
University of Texas Press, Austin, 1965. 132 pp. $4.95
(original title: *Vidas sêcas*)

188   **Rêgo, José Lins do**   *Brazil*
PLANTATION BOY
Translated by Emmi Baum
Knopf, New York, 1966. 530 pp. $6.95
(original title: *Menino de Engenho*)

189   **Revueltas, José**   *Mexico*
THE STONE KNIFE*
Translated by H. R. Hays
Reynal & Hitchcock, New York, 1947. 183 pp.
(original title: *El luto humano*)

190   **Reyles, Carlos**   *Uruguay*
CASTANETS*
Translated by Jacques Le Clerq
David McKay, Longmans, Green, New York, 1929. 297 pp.
(original title: *El embrujo de Sevilla*)

191   **Rivera, José Eustasio**   *Colombia*
THE VORTEX*
Translated by Earle K. James
G. P. Putnam & Sons, New York, 1935. 320 pp.
(original title: *La vorágine*)

192 Robles Soler, Antonio J. *Mexico*
THE REFUGEE CENTAUR*
Translated by Edward and Elizabeth Huberman
Twayne Publishers, New York, 1952. 245 pp.
(original title: *El refugiado Centauro Flores, novela al día*)

193 Rojas, Manuel *Chile*
BORN GUILTY*
Translated by Frank Gaynor
Library Publishers, New York, 1955. 314 pp.
(original title: *Hijo de ladrón*)

194 Romero, José Rubén *Mexico*
THE FUTILE LIFE OF PITO PEREZ*
Translated by W. Cord
Prentice-Hall, New York, 1967. 151 pp. $4.95
(original title: *La vida inútil de Pito Pérez*)

195 Romero, Pepe *Mexico*
A MILLION PESOS*
Anonymous translation
Doubleday, New York, 1964. 183 pp. $3.95
(original title not available)

196 Rosa, João Guimarães *Brazil*
THE DEVIL TO PAY IN THE BACKLANDS
Translated by James L. Taylor and Harriet de Onís
Knopf, New York, 1963. 494 pp. $5.95
(original title: *Grande sertão: Veredas*)

197 Rulfo, Juan *Mexico*
PEDRO PÁRAMO
Translated by Lysander Kemp
Grove Press, New York, 1959. 128 pp. $2.74; Evergreen edition,
    1969, $1.25 (paper)
(original edition: *Pedro Páramo*)

198 Sábato, Ernesto *Argentina*
THE OUTSIDER*
Translated by Harriet de Onís
Knopf, New York, 1950. 180 pp. $2.50
(original title: *El túnel*)

199 Sáinz, Gustavo *Mexico*
GAZAPO
Translated by Hardie St. Martin
Farrar, Straus & Giroux, New York, 1968. 181 pp. $4.95
(original title: *Gazapo*)

200 Schroeder, Agustina *Uruguay*
MOTHER OF FAIR LOVE*
Translated by Veronica Kirtland
Bruce Publishing Co., Milwaukee, 1957. 195 pp.
(original title not available)

201 Setubal, Paulo de Oliveira *Brazil*
DOMITILA, THE ROMANCE OF AN EMPEROR'S
   MISTRESS*
Translated by Margaret Richardson
Coward-McCann, New York, 1930. 324 pp.
(original title: *A marquesa de Santos*)

202 Spota, Luis *Mexico*
THE WOUNDS OF HUNGER*
Translated by Barnaby Conrad
Houghton Mifflin, Boston, 1957. 233 pp.
(original title: *Más cornadas da el hambre*)

203 Spota, Luis
THE ENEMY BLOOD*
Translated by Robert Malloy
Doubleday, New York, 1961. 308 pp. $3.95
(original title: *La sangre enemiga*)

204 Spota, Luis
*THE TIME OF WRATH***
Translated by Robert Malloy
Doubleday, New York, 1962. 465 pp. $5.95
(original title: *El tiempo de la ira*)

205 Spota, Luis
*ALMOST PARADISE***
Translated by Roy and Renate Morrison
Doubleday, New York, 1963. 391 pp. $4.95
(original title: *Casi el Paraíso*)

206 Subercaseaux, Benjamín *Chile*
*JEMMY BUTTON***
Translated by Mary and Fred del Villar
Macmillan, New York, 1954. 382 pp.
(original title: *Jemmy Button*)

207 Taunay, Alfredo D'Escragnolle *Brazil*
*INOCÊNCIA***
Translated by Henriqueta Chamberlain
Macmillan, New York, 1945. 209 pp.
(original title: *Innocência*)

208 Uslar Pietri, Arturo *Venezuela*
*THE RED LANCES***
Translated by Harriet de Onís
Knopf, New York, 1963. 233 pp. $4.95
(original title: *Las lanzas coloradas*)

209 Vargas Llosa, Mario *Peru*
THE TIME OF THE HERO
Translated by Lysander Kemp
Grove Press, New York, 1966. 409 pp. $5.95
(original title: *La ciudad y los perros*)

210 Vargas Llosa, Mario
THE GREEN HOUSE
Translated by Gregory Rabassa
Harper and Row, New York, 1967. 405 pp. $6.95
(original title: *La casa verde*)

211 Verissimo, Erico *Brazil*
*CROSSROADS**
Translated by L. C. Kaplan
Macmillan, New York, 1943. 373 pp.
(original title: *Caminhos cruzados*)

212 Verissimo, Erico
*THE REST IS SILENCE**
Translated by L. C. Kaplan
Macmillan, New York, 1946. 485 pp.
(original title: *O resto e silêncio*)

213 Verissimo, Erico
*CONSIDER THE LILIES OF THE FIELD**
Translated by Jean Neel Karnoff
Macmillan, New York, 1947. 371 pp.
(original title: *Olhai os lírios do campo*)

214 Verissimo, Erico
*TIME AND THE WIND**
Translated by L. L. Barrett
Macmillan, New York, 1951. 624 pp.
(original title: *O tempo e o vento*)

215 Verissimo, Erico
*NIGHT**
Translated by L. L. Barrett
Macmillan, New York, 1956. 166 pp.
(original title: *Noite*)

216 Verissimo, Erico
*HIS EXCELLENCY, THE AMBASSADOR**
Translated by Linton Lomas Barrett and Marie McDavid Barrett
Macmillan, New York, 1966. 439 pp. $6.95
(original title: *O Senhor Embaixador*)

217 Villaverde, Cirilo *Cuba*
*THE QUADROON OR CECILIA VALDÉS**
Translated by Mariano J. Lorente
Farrar, Straus & Giroux, New York, 1935. 399 pp.
(original title: *Cecilia Valdés o la loma del ángel*)

218 Villaverde, Cirilo
*CECILIA VALDÉS, A NOVEL OF CUBAN CUSTOMS**
Translated by Sydney G. Gest
Vantage Press, New York, 1962. 546 pp.
(original title: *Cecilia Valdés*)

219 Wast, Hugo (pseud. of Gustavo Martínez Zuviria)   *Argentina*
*BLACK VALLEY, A ROMANCE OF THE ARGENTINE**
Translated by Herman and Miriam Hespelt
Longmans, Green, New York, 1928. 302 pp.
(original title: *Valle negro*)

220 Wast, Hugo
*STONE DESERT**
Translated by Louis Imbert and Jacques Le Clerq
Longmans, Green, New York, 1928. 302 pp.
(original title: *El desierto de piedra*)

221 Wast, Hugo
*PEACH BLOSSOM**
Translated by Herman and Miriam Hespelt
Longmans, Green, New York, 1929. 300 pp.
(original title: *Flor de durazno*)

222 Wast, Hugo
*THE STRENGTH OF LOVERS**
Translated by Louis Imbert and Jacques Le Clerq
Longmans, Green, New York, 1930. 315 pp.
(original title: *Lucía Miranda*)

223 Yáñez, Agustín   *Mexico*
THE EDGE OF THE STORM
Translated by Ethel Brinton
University of Texas Press, Austin, 1963. 332 pp. $6.50
(original title: *Al filo del agua*)

224 Yáñez, Agustín
THE LEAN LANDS
Translated by Ethel Brinton
University of Texas Press, Austin, 1968. 328 pp. $6.50
(original title: *Las tierras flacas*)

Indexes *Figures refer to item numbers*

AUTHORS

ERRATA

On pages 20 and 21 for "Santo Domingo" *read* "Dominican Republic"

INDEX REVISIONS

The contents of 24a are indexed under 24

AUTHORS
Arreola, Juan José, *add* 75
Add Gonzalez de Eslava, Fernán, 2 *after* González B., Jorge
Neto, Coelho, *delete* 4, *add* 5
Pagaza, Joaquín Arcadio, *add* 3

ORIGINAL TITLES
Amalia, *delete* 129
Bahía de silencio, La, *delete* 171, *add* 173
Bomarzo, *delete* 132
Lucía Miranda, *delete* 173

ENGLISH TITLES
Blow-Up, *delete* 43, *add* 81
Cross and the Sword, The, *delete* 60, *add* 149
Portrait of a Paladin, *delete* 70, *add* 160

COUNTRIES
Argentina, *add* 77–81, 155
Bolivia, *delete* 35, *add* 133
Brazil, *add* 87, 165, 201
Chile, *add* 160
Cuba, *add* 11
Dominican Republic, *add* 23
Mexico, *add* 46, 224
Nicaragua, *add* 4
Peru, *add* 96
Uruguay, *add* 90

ORIGINAL TITLES

ENGLISH TITLES

COUNTRIES

ARGENTINA	1, 8, 10, 11, 16–29, 31, 32, 45, 69, 74a, 76, 82, 84, 120, 131, 132, 134, 139, 150, 151, 154, 156, 164, 173–175, 179, 198, 219–222
BOLIVIA	1, 8, 16, 19, 23, 24, 28, 35
BRAZIL	1, 5, 8, 10, 11, 13, 14, 19, 31, 34, 35, 47, 74, 86, 91, 92, 99, 101–105, 107, 108, 113, 125, 130, 138, 140, 141, 167–171, 185–188, 196, 207, 211–216
CHILE	1, 4, 6, 8, 10, 11, 16–25, 27, 28, 30–32, 42, 48–60, 64, 66, 67, 85, 94, 97, 98, 118, 122, 123, 123a, 136, 137, 159, 163, 182, 183, 193, 206
COLOMBIA	1, 8, 10, 11, 16, 17, 19, 23–25, 27, 28, 31, 32, 65, 83, 162, 176, 191
COSTA RICA	1, 17, 23, 24
CUBA	1, 7, 9, 10, 15, 17, 19–25, 27, 28, 31–33, 42a, 44, 109, 109a, 126–128, 217, 218
DOMINICAN REPUBLIC	9, 10, 24, 25, 149
ECUADOR	1, 8, 17, 19, 20, 22–25, 30, 32, 36, 37, 94a, 153, 161
EL SALVADOR	1, 17, 23
GUATEMALA	1, 10, 17, 23, 24, 27, 28, 31, 110–112a
HONDURAS	1, 10, 23, 24
MEXICO	1–4, 8, 10–12, 15–25, 27, 28, 30–32, 43, 61–63, 68, 68a, 70, 71, 75, 88, 93, 100, 114–117, 124, 129, 142–147, 152, 157, 158, 166, 172, 177, 178, 189, 192, 194, 195, 197, 199, 202–205, 223
NICARAGUA	1, 10, 15–17, 19, 20, 23–25, 28, 39, 40, 41
PANAMA	1, 8, 17, 23
PARAGUAY	1, 17, 23, 24, 31
PERU	1, 4, 8, 10, 11, 15–20, 22, 23–26, 28, 31, 32, 38, 72, 73, 89, 95, 209, 210
URUGUAY	1, 8, 10, 11, 16, 17, 19–29, 31, 73a, 106, 119, 140a, 180, 190, 200
VENEZUELA	1, 8, 10, 17, 19, 23, 24, 27, 31, 32, 121, 135, 148, 181, 184, 208